# Grammar Workbook 4

Contents

Unit 1	Word classes	page 2
Unit 2	Using standard English	page 4
Unit 3	Active and passive verbs 1	page 6
Unit 4	Connectives	page 8
Unit 5	Forming complex sentences 1	page 10
Unit 6	Punctuation	page 12
Unit 8	Active and passive verbs 2	page 14
Unit 9	Official language	page 16
Unit 10	Forming complex sentences 2	page 18
Unit 11	Making notes	page 20
Unit 12	Writing a summary	page 22
Unit 13	Editing	page 24
Unit 14	Conditional sentences	page 27
Unit 16	Narrative writing	page 30
Unit 17	Describing past events	page 33
Unit 18	Giving instructions	page 36
Unit 19	Writing reports	page 38
Unit 20	Persuasive writing	page 41
Unit 21	Writing discussion texts	page 44
Unit 22	Investigating English expressions	page 47

unit 1 Word classes

🔑 Key idea

Words are categorised in classes according to the jobs they do in a sentence: noun, pronoun, verb, adjective, adverb, preposition, conjunction and interjection. Words can belong to more than one class.

Work it out

Give one-word answers. *(10 marks)*

1 Which proper noun is the name of the Italian capital? _____
2 Which adjective is the opposite of "wise"? _____
3 Which collective noun means "a lot of (birds flying) together"? _____
4 Which verb means "to tremble with cold or fear"? _____
5 Which pronoun is the opposite of "no one"? _____
6 Which proper noun is the name of the shortest month of the year? _____
7 Which adverb is the opposite of "rarely"? _____
8 What is the second part of the conjunction "not only…"? _____
9 What adverb can we form from "skill"? _____
10 Which verb means to "make longer"? _____

Which word?

Ring or underline the right word in the brackets. *(10 marks)*

1 It was dark, so we couldn't see (nothing, anything) clearly.
2 Would you mind (to wait, waiting) a few minutes?
3 There (are, is) more than one way of solving this problem.
4 Where (are, is) the rest of the players?
5 The change in the plan will not have a great deal of (affect, effect) on us.
6 Don't be so (impatience, impatient), John!
7 Between you and (I, me), I think Margaret is quite right to be suspicious.
8 This photo is different (than, from) that one.
9 We watched the marathon, but we did not (took, take) part in it.
10 Your new bike is much better than (Paul's, Pauls').

Classify it

Read this passage from *Nicholas Nickleby* by Charles Dickens. Place each of the underlined words under the correct heading in the grid below. *(10 marks – 0.5 mark for each correctly placed word)*

Dotheboy's Hall <u>was</u> not a hall at all, <u>but</u> a bare and dirty room with a <u>couple</u> of windows, in which most of the glass was broken. There were a few old <u>rickety</u> desks, <u>cut</u> and notched, and inked and damaged, in <u>every</u> possible way; a detached desk for <u>Squeers</u>; and another <u>for</u> his assistant. The ceiling was supported, like <u>that</u> of a barn, by cross beams and rafters; and the walls were so stained that it was impossible to tell <u>whether</u> they had ever been painted or whitewashed.

But the pupils! How his last hopes <u>faded</u> as <u>he</u> looked <u>around</u>! Pale and haggard faces of old men, boys of stunted growth, and others whose long thin legs would <u>hardly</u> carry their <u>stooping</u> bodies, all <u>crowded</u> together; there were the bleary eye, the hare-lip, the crooked foot, and every problem arising from <u>cruelty</u> and neglect. There were little faces which should have been handsome, darkened with the scowl of suffering; there were vicious-faced boys, brooding like prisoners in jail; <u>and</u> there were children <u>who</u> were weeping <u>with</u> loneliness…

nouns	
pronouns	
verbs	
adjectives	
adverbs	
prepositions	
conjunctions	

# Unit 2

Using standard English

Key idea

We can use non-standard English in speech, but we must use standard English in formal written work.

Does it agree?

Underline the subject each time. (It may be a single word or a group of words.) Then circle the right word in the brackets so that the verb agrees with its subject.
(14 marks)

1 How much of the information in newspaper reports or radio and television news reports (are, is) completely accurate?

2 According to a report on television, a reward of several thousand pounds (has, have) been offered for information leading to the arrest of the robbers.

3 The driver of the bus – together with two of the passengers – (was, were) slightly injured in the accident.

4 (Is, Are) there any mud on your shoes?

5 The number of flights from London to Spain (have, has) risen in recent years because more people like to spend a holiday on the Spanish coast.

6 There (is, are) a number of reasons why people prefer to spend their holiday abroad. The main attraction is the better climate overseas.

7 What a nuisance! All the traffic (has, have) stopped. There must have been an accident somewhere ahead of us.

8 Before the play started, a member of the cast peeped through the curtains and said, "Oh, good! The audience (is, are) a really big one tonight. There are no empty seats."

9 Everybody in our class (want, wants) to join in the picnic, don't they?

10 How long (has, have) all this rubbish been lying here?

11 As a result of a change in the law, the poor (is, are) likely to be better off.

12 A good standard of numeracy (is, are) necessary in many jobs.

13 At least a third of those players (is, are) from foreign countries.

14 The majority of the pupils in our class (does, do) not come to school in a car.

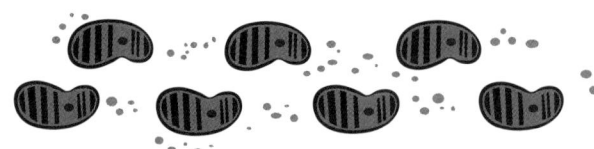

Choose the right word

Ring or underline the right words in the brackets. *(8 marks)*

1 This shop doesn't sell cosmetics (or, nor) health foods.

2 My sister doesn't like garlic and (so, nor) do I.

3 Sometimes people are not sure where to keep their money. If they hide (them, it) at home, there is always a risk of burglary.

4 The manager told his staff that he hadn't (no, any) intention of resigning.

5 John did not feel very well at the start of the cross-country race, and he felt much (worse, worser) at the end.

6 After the show, my friend and (me, I) bought some chips and ate (it, them) on the way home.

7 We need somebody to check all the electrical (equipment, equipments) before we turn on the computer and heating.

8 Our visit to Scandinavia (maybe, may be) described as a tour rather than a holiday.

Make it formal

Write more formal expressions that we can use instead of the italic words. *(8 marks)*

1 That's a *lousy* idea. _____

2 There's a rumour that their business is *on the rocks*. _____

3 All the *kids* in my class agree with me. _____

4 I haven't got *nothing* special to tell you. _____

5 The man said he didn't know *no one* with that name. _____

6 The fact that he is guilty *sticks out like a sore thumb*. _____

7 This hairstyle is gradually *catching on*. _____

8 *How come* you're not at school today? _____

unit 3 Active and passive verbs 1

Key idea

Verbs can be in the **active** or **passive** voice.

A dangerous job

Write in the *passive* Simple Present form of the verbs in brackets. *(12 marks)*

In Malaysia, rubber (1) _____ (grow) on many estates. At dawn, rubber-tappers start work. Many of them are women and they know that their work can be dangerous. Sometimes tappers (2) _____ (attack) by a tiger. When they bend down to tap a tree, they (3) _____ (sometimes mistake) for a wild animal and attacked by a hungry tiger.

Tappers start work before the sun rises. First, a cut (4) _____ (make) in a mature tree. A tin or half a coconut shell (5) _____ (fasten) to the tree. It (6) _____ (use) to collect latex from the cut. The tapper cuts many trees. Then he or she returns to the first tree. Latex in the tin (7) _____ (empty) into a pail which (8) _____ (take) to the small "factory" on the estate. Chemicals (9) _____ (add) to the latex and mixed in well. Later on, the latex (10) _____ (squeeze) into sheets which (11) _____ (hang) in a smoke-filled hut. Finally, the sheets of rubber (12) _____ (tie) up in bales, ready for export to other countries.

A gas leak

Put in the *passive* form of the verbs in brackets. Use *has/have been* + *a past participle* each time. *(10 marks)*

One evening Mrs Wilson (Mrs W) was on her way home from work. She got off a bus and started to walk the 200 metres to her home. As she walked round a corner, she was surprised to see a crowd of people outside a wrecked house. There were fire-engines and police cars there too. Mrs Wilson's friend, Mrs Johnson (Mrs J), was in the crowd.

Mrs W: What's the matter? What's happened?

Mrs J: There was a gas leak. That house (1) _____ (wreck) completely.

Mrs W: (2) _____ anybody _____ (injure)?

Mrs J: Yes, two people (3) _____ (hurt). They (4) _____ (take) to hospital already.

Mrs W: What are the fire-engines doing here?

Mrs J: There was a small fire but it (5) _____ (bring) under control. The gas company (6) _____ (inform), so men are coming to repair the pipe. A lot of debris (7) _____ (hurl) across the road, so the windows in those houses (8) _____ (break). The people in those houses (9) _____ (evacuate). There were some elderly people in that old folks' home over there. They (10) _____ (move) to another home temporarily.

Mrs W: Is there anything we can do to help?

Mrs J: No, I don't think so.

In trouble

Put in the *passive* future form of the verbs in brackets. Use *will be + a past participle*. *(8 marks)*

Paul's friend, Mike, was sent off during a football match for hitting an opponent. Now Paul is asking his dad, a referee, what will happen to Mike.

Paul: Will Mike get into trouble?

Dad: Yes, I'm afraid he will. I'm sure he (1) _____ (charge) with hitting an opponent. Then he (2) _____ (ask) to attend a hearing before the Disciplinary Committee. He (3) _____ (tell) what he is charged with.

Paul: What will happen after that?

Dad: He (4) _____ (give) a chance to listen to the referee's report and ask any questions. Then he (5) _____ (invite) to make his statement and admit the charge or try to deny it.

Paul: I don't think he will deny it because everybody saw what happened. What will the Committee do?

Dad: Well, Mike (6) _____ (inform) of the decision in writing. It is probable that he (7) _____ (ban) for a few months. If he has a bad record, he (8) _____ (fine) as well, I should think.

Unit 4 Connectives

Key idea

Connectives are words and phrases that are used to link different parts of a text. They can join words, phrases, clauses, sentences and paragraphs.

Types of connectives

Underline the connectives in the sentences below. Then put them under the correct heading in the grid. *(10 marks)*

1 Paul decided to buy the bicycle although it was expensive.

2 We can go out when the rain stops.

3 Mary stuck a stamp on the envelope and then she posted the invitation.

4 Following my operation, I developed an infection in the wound.

5 We can go for a picnic on Saturday if the weather is good.

6 Mike can't go out to play now because he hasn't finished his homework yet.

7 You can go to London by train or you can travel on the express bus.

8 Our new house is bigger than our old one. Moreover, it has a large garden.

9 Most people like Susan, but I think she is rather conceited.

10 Despite having a terrible cold, the soprano performed her solo.

Addition	Time	Cause and effect	Opposition

Connective starters

Complete each sentence in a suitable way to show that you understand the connective. *(10 marks)*

1 We'll have to wait here until _____

2 If you eat too much, _____

3 We couldn't move the wardrobe because _____

4 Although it snowed last night, _____

5 In spite of the cold weather, _____

6 Kate is very fond of animals, so _____

7 Choose your sweets and then _____

8 I forgot to set the alarm. As a result, _____

9 The game started on time despite _____

10 I often eat fish. However, _____

Choosing connectives

Ring or underline the right word in the brackets. *(10 marks)*

1 We can go there by taxi. (Alternately, Alternatively) we can take the bus.

2 (Despite, In spite) the discount, Mrs Lee decided not to buy the car.

3 We had to leave our house when a pipe burst. Now we're waiting for the workmen to complete the repairs. In the (while, meantime), we're staying with my grandparents.

4 The team has succeeded because the owner of the club is a billionaire. (Nevertheless, Furthermore) it has one of the best managers in Europe.

5 Crocodiles have no predators to attack them. (Consequently, Subsequently) they manage to live for many years.

6 Trees can spread their seeds in many ways. (Meanwhile, For example,) sycamore seeds have "wings" to help them fly away from the parent tree.

7 We don't agree with Paul's plan. On the (other hand, contrary), we think it could be disastrous for the club.

8 His plan contains several faults. (Nevertheless, Similarly) it contains some good points.

9 You ought to buy yourself a watch (instead of, in spite of) borrowing mine.

10 Most shops have security cameras (providing, so that) they can catch thieves.

Unit 5 Forming complex sentences 1

Key idea

Complex sentences are made up of more than one clause. The clauses can be joined in different ways.

Completing sentences

**Complete these sentences in any sensible way.
Draw a ring round the connecting words.** *(10 marks)*

1 A library is a place where _____

2 There was a hidden cottage where _____

3 Don't forget to turn the lights off when _____

4 People go to a dentist when _____

5 Plants will usually grow well if _____

6 Traffic police may stop a motorist if _____

7 Mary had the flu last week, so _____

8 Paul could not hear what people were saying on television, so _____
   _____

9 You can go to your friend's house now, provided that _____
   _____

10 You can borrow my bike if you like, provided that _____
   _____

What and where?

Complete each sentence by saying *what* people are doing and *where* they are doing it. Start with a present participle (an –ing word) *(10 marks)*

Example: We watched some men **repairing** a pipe in the road near our home.

1 Ashra heard two women _____

2 When I came out of my house, I noticed a man _____
   _____

3 When we reached the beach, we saw some fishermen _____
   _____

4 Before we entered the park, we stopped to watch some boys _____

5 When Sue looked out of the window, she saw a blackbird _____

6 Last night on television we watched some girls _____

7 After a few minutes, the fox came to a field and was happy to see some lambs _____

8 Mr Evans woke up during the night when he heard somebody _____

9 When our bus passed Mary's house, we saw her father _____

10 The lifeguard ran down the beach when he heard somebody _____

Punctuating complex sentences

Put in the missing commas. *(10 marks)*

1 Yesterday in broad daylight the police caught two men trying to rob a bank.

2 The frightened rabbit stayed absolutely still hoping that the fox had not seen it.

3 My father the manager of the store starts work before 8 a.m.

4 Last night the temperature in most Welsh towns was above freezing-point. In Aberystwyth however it was minus four degrees.

5 Did you enjoy yourself at the party last Saturday Kate?

6 Although the concert lasted for over two hours the audience was captivated by the soloist who was only ten.

7 Not having seen her cousin for several years Sue was surprised to see how tall he was.

8 Birmingham is a very large city. In fact it is one of the largest in the United Kingdom.

9 When the phone rang Peter hurried to answer it hoping that it was his friend.

10 Leaping over the wall the frightened animal disappeared into the woods.

Punctuation

Key idea

Adding clauses increases the complexity of sentences, so more punctuation is required.

Using commas

Put in commas where necessary. The sentences show various different uses of commas. *(10 marks)*

1 The home of the Duke of Devonshire has 173 rooms and houses more than 60 types of clocks.

2 Paul go and find Mary please.

3 Worms are probably the most common bait for fish. If you expect to catch fish therefore you must be prepared to handle worms.

4 'Ugh! I'm not going to touch a worm' Katie said.

5 One of our neighbours Mrs Collins is a very experienced nurse.

6 Even if I were a billionaire I would not want to live alone in a huge isolated house.

7 Very few people read poetry books in their leisure time. Many modern pop songs however contain their own type of poetry and are very popular.

8 When tadpoles get older their tails get shorter their legs get longer and they gradually develop into very small frogs.

9 Pauline Taylor whose father is a maths teacher is always top of the class in maths not surprisingly.

10 If you're ready it's time for us to leave for the airport Grandad.

Using speech marks

Each of these unpunctuated sentences contains direct speech. Rewrite them, putting in the speech marks and other punctuation marks and capital letters that are necessary. *(10 marks)*

1 My friend said to me would you mind checking this letter for me please

2 I told her you've left an r out of preferred

3 Miss Lee told me you should have written chose and not choose

4 I heard Paul shout out wait for me Mike so we waited for him

5 If you've finished your homework my mother said you can watch the film on TV

6 when the performance ended the audience rose to their feet and shouted bravo

7 clamouring up the treacherous rocks the mountain rescuer cried hold on

8 can i follow you asked grace i dont know the way besides its dark

9 the wizard whose wand was misbehaving shook his finger and said abracadabra

10 louise rubbed her eyes yawned and mumbled whats the matter

More punctuation practice

Put in any necessary punctuation marks and capital letters. *(10 marks)*

1 its the end of march tomorrow remember to put your clocks on an hour

2 remember what people say in america spring forward fall back

3 in sentence 2 the word fall means autumn

4 there are 24 children in our class 14 boys and 10 girls

5 i think that jacket is a real bargain don't you mary

6 that was my first visit to a zoo I thought it was very interesting

7 come in sit down would you like a soft drink

8 some girls like to play netball or rounders others prefer hockey

9 the speaker promised the people many things more jobs higher pay longer holidays and lower taxes

10 don't forget the saying nothing ventured nothing gained

Active and passive verbs 2

Key idea

Verbs can be in the **active** or **passive** voice.

Look to the future

Read the two passages. Write in the *passive* future form of the verbs in brackets.
(10 marks)

A. Tomorrow part of the motorway (1)_____ (close) for urgent resurfacing. The work (2)_____ (complete) by 4 p.m., when the road (3)_____ (reopen) to traffic. While the road is closed, traffic (4)_____ (divert). Notices (5)_____ (put) up to show motorists the route to follow.

B. Miss Harris told her class, "Our Sports Day will be on next Friday. It (6)_____ (hold) on the school field, starting at noon. All lessons will be (7)_____ (cancel) for the afternoon of that day. All parents (8)_____ (invite) to come. If bad weather is forecast, you (9)_____ (tell) and Sports Day (10)_____ (postpone) to the following week."

Will, may or must?

Read these sentences carefully. Then decide whether to put in *will*, *may* or *must*.
(10 marks)

1 This letter is urgent. It _____ be posted as soon as possible.

2 During a thunderstorm, don't shelter under a tree. It _____ be hit by lightning. If it is hit, you _____ be killed or seriously injured.

3 Be careful if you see an adder. It is a venomous snake with black zigzag marks on its top. Don't go near or touch an adder. If you do, you _____ be bitten. Then you _____ be taken to hospital. You _____ be given an antidote to fight the venom from the snake.

4 Check your bike before you go for a long ride. The brakes _____ be checked and the tyres _____ be pumped up if necessary.

5 When people return from a holiday overseas, their passports _____ be checked by an Immigration Officer. Then their luggage _____ be searched by a Customs Officer.

Active to passive

Change these sentences so that they contain *passive* verbs instead of active ones. Leave out the italic words. *(10 marks)*

1 *Somebody* stole Mr Jackson's car during the night.
_____

2 Before the dentist drilled my tooth, *she* gave me an injection.
_____

3 *Some workmen* pulled down that old factory last week.
_____

4 *The strong wind* blew down two trees last night.
_____

5 *Somebody* has just taken Mrs Sharpe to hospital.
_____

6 *Two dustmen* collect our rubbish every Friday.
_____

7 *People* grow a lot of apples in this part of the country.
_____

8 *Sharks or other large fish* sometimes attack swimmers not far from the beach.
_____

9 *The Mayor* will open the new school tomorrow.
_____

10 *Several workmen* will redecorate our school during the holidays.
_____

# unit 9
Official language

 **Key idea**

Formal and official documents have certain language features that distinguish them from informal writing.

Informal: first person (personal); colloquial/slang vocabulary; use of contractions; short, simple sentences; exclamations, questions

Formal: third person (impersonal); technical, subject-specific vocabulary; no contractions; complex sentences; statements

---

Len Benton sent his friend, Mary Evans, a fake formal letter from a firm of solicitors when she wanted to borrow his bicycle. Mary decided to continue the game with Len. She sent him this invitation to her birthday party.

> On behalf of Miss Mary Evans, we have very considerable pleasure in requesting the pleasure of your company at a sumptuous festive social gathering of young attractive females and boisterous males to celebrate the eleventh anniversary of her blessed nativity.
>
> Please be informed accordingly that this joyful event will take place at Miss Evans' ancestral place of residence at 462 Rowan Road on Saturday 25 April, commencing punctually at 4 p.m. and drawing to a close by 8 p.m.
>
> To enable us to make adequate preparations, we would greatly appreciate it if you would kindly get in touch with us and indicate whether or not you will be able to join all concerned in this celebration. Kindly let us know what you decide before noon on 21 April so that our plans may be finalised well in advance. Alternatively, you may prefer to make your decision known directly to Mary (by phone, email, fax or in person).
>
> We are asked to pass on to all guests Mary's particular request that presents should not be brought or sent.

What do they mean?

Find and underline the expressions in Mary's invitation that have these meanings.
(10 marks)

1 are happy   3 party   5 birthday   7 home   9 would like
2 to invite   4 children   6 note (verb)   8 finishing   10 everybody

In translation

Len's brother asked him what was in the letter from Mary. Pretend you are Len. Tell your brother – in everyday English – what the main points of the invitation are. *(10 marks)*

_____
_____
_____
_____
_____
_____

Keep it simple

Give the meaning of the expressions in italics. Use ordinary, everyday English that makes the meaning clear but uses fewer words. *(10 marks)*

1 Please *contact him in writing*. _____

2 Write your name here, *giving your surname and all given names*.
   _____

3 *In the event that* you are unable to come, bring a note when you recover.
   _____

4 Mike missed a lot of lessons at school *as a result* of illness.
   _____

5 Ask a parent or *the person who is legally responsible for looking after you* to write a note to your teacher, explaining why you were absent.
   _____

6 Peter cannot come today because he is *suffering from some illness*.
   _____

7 The *man who has been accused of robbery but has not yet been tried or convicted* will give evidence tomorrow.
   _____

8 Mr Macdonald is a farmer, so he would like to *wipe out and completely get rid of* all the rabbits on his farm.
   _____

9 Your claim for compensation will be *studied in detail to ascertain all aspects of the problem*.
   _____

10 You will be told *what is eventually decided by officials who look into your case*.
   _____

Forming complex sentences 2

Key idea

subordinate clause   main clause   subordinate clause

After the party, we all went straight home because it was late.

There are different types of subordinate clauses. They are linked to the main clause with connectives.

Adding connectives

Put one of the following connectives in each blank space below. *(10 marks)*

if	after	before	although	when	so
while	despite	provided	so	that	

1 I have a poster that reminds me to wash my hands _____ I have a meal, and to clean my teeth _____ I have eaten anything.

2 _____ Mum agrees, we're going to have a barbecue this evening _____ it doesn't rain.

3 The house in Elm Street was too expensive and _____ my parents decided not to buy it _____ we all liked it very much

4 You can borrow these videos but let me have them back _____ Mary can watch them _____ she returns from holiday.

5 The fire started _____ men were carrying out repairs. It destroyed the whole building _____ the efforts of the firemen.

Punctuating complex sentences

Punctuate these sentences correctly. Don't forget to put in capital letters where necessary. *(10 marks – 2 marks for each correct sentence)*

1 we expected toms friend to come at 5 pm however he didnt arrive until 530

2 in the middle of lunch a boy rushed into the canteen shouting fire fire

3 I put my books away and turned off the light then I went to bed

4 when the phone rang maya picked it up expecting to hear her friends voice

5 the answer peter gave although partially correct was not the right one

Joining sentences

Join each group of sentences to make one sentence. You can change, add or omit words. *(10 marks – 2.5 marks for each correct sentence)*

1 The rain stopped. We played in the garden. The grass was still wet. We were quite chilly.

2 The girl won lots of money. She gave half of it to charity. She is Janet's cousin.

3 This is the ring. My aunt gave it to me. I was ten then. It is beautiful.

4 Uncle George is over fifty. He completed the marathon. He raised lots of money for charity.

Making notes

Key idea

We make notes to extract the most important points from written words (such as information text) or spoken words (such as a telephone conversation or interview). We write them down in a shorter form.

Babysitting

You are babysitting for Mrs Done. You receive some phone calls and need to jot down notes so that you can write out messages for her. Make notes. *(10 marks)*

1 Is that Connie Jackson? Oh, well, maybe I could leave a message for her. My name is Peter Brown. I was going to call on her tomorrow at her office at about ten but something has come up, so I can't make it. Please ask her to phone my secretary at 099-438 tomorrow to fix another appointment. Thursday or Friday would be fine for me, ideally in the morning. Thanks. Goodbye.

2 Can I interest you in a good deal on double-glazing? This week we're offering … Oh, I see. Hmmm. Well, perhaps you'd tell her that Glunk Glass have this special offer next week, for seven days only. We're offering a discount of twenty-five per cent for two windows or more. If further details are needed, ask the lady to phone Andrew Brown at 047-738 any time. Thanks.

Customer services

You are learning the work in the Customer Services Department of a busy store. People phone, so you have to take notes and then tell the manager what the complaint is about. Read what these people said to you. Make notes. *(10 marks)*

1 My name's Ivy Trott. What's that? No, I'm not related to her. What I want to do is complain about the Milky Way Mousse. Don't get me wrong. I like them very much, but you never seem to have any in stock. What's happened? Are the staff eating them all? How come you've never got any on sale? Please ask somebody to order some more, pronto!

2   I want to complain about the tomatoes in your fruit and vegetable section. I usually buy a packet of six. Twice I've found that two of the tomatoes were bad underneath. They look all right on top but when you get them out – that's a different story. Maybe you could have a word with your order clerk or whoever does the ordering and change your supplier. I'll check up on them in the coming weeks and let you know if I see any improvement. I will be bringing back the two bad ones I bought this week and will expect a refund.

Local newspaper reporter

You are a reporter in the office of a local newspaper. You receive these phone calls. Make notes of the important points. *(10 marks)*

1   In the past week, six cars have been damaged by hooligans in Leo's car park. Each of them had a window broken. One had its tyres slashed. Three had the paintwork scratched badly. The damage occurs between about 10 p.m. and 6 a.m. I can tell you the names and addresses of a couple of louts who hang out there if you're interested.

2   You ought to investigate a house in Lufton Road. It's number 39 There's something fishy going on there. It's been empty for about six months, but recently the lights have been on and I've seen a lot of people coming and going with huge boxes at all hours of the day. There are often five or six lorries parked in the road at a time. There's a problem with burglary in our area at the moment. Perhaps the house is being used to store stolen goods.

unit 12 Writing a summary

Key idea

A summary is a re-telling in a shorter number of words of something you have read or heard.
- Summaries require writing in complete sentences.
- Summaries should include the main idea and important points only.

One-word summaries

In each case, give one word that summarises the group of words below. *(10 marks)*

1. a place where water is stored so that it can be sent to homes
   _____

2. walking along slowly and hardly lifting the feet off the ground
   _____

3. a long hole through a hill, often for a railway line
   _____

4. a place where people can keep their money and earn interest
   _____

5. a man or woman who looks after sick or injured people
   _____

6. wet stuff that comes trickling down from the clouds
   _____

7. biting and biting and biting (when the food is tough)
   _____

8. not liking to be delayed or kept waiting for anything
   _____

9. taken into custody (by a police officer)
   _____

10. in a way showing considerable skill
    _____

Headlines

Make up five newspaper headlines (of not more than six words each). *(10 marks – 2 marks for each one)*

1 A mineshaft has opened under a house in a village near Durham, causing half the house to disappear down the shaft. Luckily, the owners were in the other half of the house and were not hurt – but they were shocked.

   _____

2 A large black animal, similar to a panther, has been seen by a farmer in a field near Taunton. Several sheep have been killed in the vicinity recently.

   _____

3 Cricketer Jason Foley has just scored 500 not out in a test match against Australia. He has earned a five-figure bonus for his achievement.

   _____

4 A girl, aged 12, fell at home, hit her head on a stone floor and became unconscious. Her mother dialled 999 but the ambulance did not arrive until an hour later. By that time, the girl was gravely ill. She died shortly after she was taken to hospital. Her parents were outraged and very angry at the delay.

   _____

5 A venomous spider was found in a bunch of grapes imported from South Africa. The purchaser spotted the spider and took it to a laboratory where it was examined and then killed. It was found to be extremely harmful. The store which sold the grapes has apologised and promised to inspect imports more thoroughly.

   _____

What can you remember?

Write a summary of each of the things below. Use a single sentence each time. Do not use more than twenty words in each sentence. *(10 marks – 2.5 marks for each sentence)*

1 A recent lesson which you enjoyed at school _____
   _____

2 What you did yesterday from 5 p.m. until the time you went to bed _____
   _____

3 The last television programme you watched _____
   _____

4 Your favourite book _____
   _____

Editing

Key idea

Editing involves reviewing and improving our own (or someone else's) writing to make it more effective.

Using more effective words

You are editing a composition written by a friend. Suggest two more effective words that could be used instead of the words in italics. Your words do not have to be synonyms of the italic words, but they should be suitable for the situation.

(10 marks – 0.5 mark for each suitable answer)

1 A group of children ran away in front of us. When we were nearly at the corner, a woman *came* out of her house. She was upset and waved her arms angrily at us.

   _____   _____

2 'Go away! Get out of here!' she *said to* us *loudly*.

   _____   _____

   _____   _____

3 The policeman *looked* at us. His face *indicated* that trouble was coming.

   _____   _____

   _____   _____

4 The old man *moved* painfully towards the receptionist.

   _____   _____

5 Mary wore a *nice* outfit to her friend's party.

   _____   _____

6 The tornado *pulled apart* the town, leaving a trail of destruction behind it.

   _____   _____

7 The poor animal *moved* towards us on its three good legs as if *asking* us to help.

   _____   _____

   _____   _____

Correcting errors

The following sentences are taken from a report by a pupil about the school canteen. Edit the sentences by correcting any mistakes in them. Write out the sentences correctly. *(10 marks – 0.5 mark for each correction)*

1 In the coarse of our investigations, we watched pupils had lunch on sevral days.

2 We noticed that some pupil had to queue a long time before they could obtained there food.

3 We therefore suggest that there should be two seperate sessions for lunch, the younger children can eat 20 minutes earlier then the oldest pupils.

4 This will also prevent the food to becoming cold and will enable the servers to work more careful, they are all in favour of this change.

5 We asked each pupil to complete a questionaire about the food, we used the information from them to produce the lists in Apendix 3

6 The tables what the pupils sit at are to crowded, so we recommend that only six pupils sit at each table, this will be possible if we have two sessions instead of one.

Using headings

(10 marks)

A classmate prepared to write a report on her school canteen. She jotted down these points:

amount of food	crowding	behaviour of pupils	servers
tables	pupil satisfaction	quality of food	cooks
cost of food	seating	cleanliness/hygiene	taste
(un)healthy food	hours/time	queues	waste

She showed you her notes and asked you for your opinion on arranging the points.

1 Suggest **five** main headings under which most or all of the points can be put.

_____
_____
_____
_____
_____

The pupils in Miss Wilson's class asked her if they could have a class picnic, so she asked them to plan the arrangements for a picnic. One pupil wrote about the following points but did not put them under any headings or in any clear order.

date	bus/car/train/coach	music/songs	weather – alternative indoors
times	food	drinks	parents – inform, come?
place	games	cost	activities

2 Suggest **five** main headings for a plan for the picnic.

_____
_____
_____
_____
_____

unit 14

Conditional sentences

Key idea

A conditional sentence says that one thing depends on another. Conditional sentences usually contain the words **if** or **unless**. The "if" or "unless" part of the sentence is a special type of subordinate clause called a **conditional clause**.

      conditional clause   main clause

<u>*If you tickle me*</u>, <u>*I will laugh.*</u>

What happens?

Complete these sentences in any sensible way. They are about habitual (usual) actions. *(10 marks – 2 marks for each correct sentence)*

1   If you leave ice out of a fridge, _____

2   If a player hits another player during a game of football, _____
_____

3   If people find that they have mice in their home, _____
_____

4   If it rains while the sun is shining, _____

5   If I'm very thirsty during the night, _____

What will probably happen?

Put in the right form of the verbs in brackets. The sentences are about things that may, can or probably will happen in future. *(5 marks – 0.5 mark for each correct answer)*

1   If a young child _____ (play) with matches at home, he or she _____ (start) a fire.

2   If it rains on Saturday, our Sports Day _____ (postpone). Then it _____ (hold) on 23 June.

3   If you _____ (eat) too much food, you _____ (put) on weight.

4   If you both stand on that table at the same time, it _____ (probably collapse) and you _____ (break) something.

5   If the rain doesn't stop soon, all this area _____ (flood) and we _____ (force) to leave our home.

Giving advice

We can use *If I were you* ... to give advice:

If I were you,	I wouldn't eat so much.
	I wouldn't bother to answer that email.
	I would be honest about it.

What advice can you give these friends or relatives? *(10 marks – 2 marks for each suitable answer)*

1 Dave says he always feels tired in the morning. He admits that he rarely goes to bed before 11 p.m. because his parents let him stay up to watch films.

   _____
   _____

2 You are visiting an aunt with your brother or sister. You have both been offered a cup of coffee, but you have declined the coffee politely. Your brother or sister is not sure whether or not to try drinking it and asks your advice.

   _____
   _____

3 A friend says she has several unwanted jigsaw puzzles at home. She is not sure whether to take them to a charity shop or just to throw them away. What do you advise?

   _____
   _____
   _____

4 A friend's family are going to spend a few days in Paris during the holidays. They can't decide whether to go by rail, ferry or air. Your friend mentioned this to you and said, "What would you do?"

   _____
   _____

5 A friend goes to a different school from yours. He tells you that he has noticed that two older boys are bullying younger pupils and making them pay money nearly every day. He is not sure what, if anything, he should do. He has asked for your advice. What do you suggest?

   _____
   _____

Other ways of showing a condition

We can also show a condition by making sentences like these:

You can go	provided that	you return before dark.
You can play with them	as long as	you're back by 700 p.m.
It's all right for you to go	on condition that	you are not late home again.

Use the information in each pair of sentences to make one sentence using one of the connectives in the second column above. You can change, omit or add words.
(5 marks)

1. You can go to Tom's house. You must be back here by 800 p.m.

2. You can borrow my bike. You must return it on Saturday.

3. Tom can stay with us for the weekend. His parents must agree.

4. I'll help you. Don't argue all the time.

5. We can have a picnic on Saturday. The weather must be fine then.

Narrative writing

 **Key idea** •••

The purpose of a narrative text is to tell a story. Although individual stories can be very different, they all have some common structural and language features.

Zangram by C. J. Salter: extract 1 •••••••••••••••

Read this extract from *Zangram*. Then answer the questions below. *(10 marks)*

> 1   The Logan family pulled wearily into a deserted car park not far from Stonehenge. Jack Logan, exhausted after driving for nine hours, said to his wife, "I need a rest."
>
>   "Good idea," his wife replied. "I told Sylvia we wouldn't be down 'til
> 5 noon."
>
>   Jack Logan glanced in the rear-view mirror. His children, Daniel and Claire, were sleeping soundly. So he settled down and was soon asleep himself.
>
>   Some time later, Claire stirred. The car seemed to be moving, but then
> 10 the movement stopped. She heard her dad snoring contentedly, and drifted back to sleep.
>
>   On board Spacecraft 462, the doors closed and a message flashed back to Zangram, far beyond Earth's solar system: "Mission completed. 20 specimens including four bipeds in a metal shell." The spaceship rose silently
> 15 from a field near Stonehenge and hurtled off into space. It carried with it the Logan family, their car, two inquisitive dogs, a deeply resentful cat and other specimens destined for examination and display in the Zangram national zoo.

1   In paragraph one, which word repeats the idea expressed by "wearily"? *(1 mark)*

2   What were Mrs Logan's exact words when she spoke to Sylvia? *(1 mark)*

3   What is missing before "Good idea" (line 4)? Why has it been left out? *(2 marks)*

4   What adverb could we use instead of each of the following? (The adverb need not have the same meaning as the given word, but it must fit the situation.) *(4 marks)*

   a) soundly (line 7) _____   c) silently (line 14) _____

   b) contentedly (line 10) _____   d) deeply (line 16) _____

5   a) What does "inquisitive" tell us about the dogs? b) Why was the cat "resentful"? *(2 marks)*

   _____

Zangram: extract 2

Read this continuation of *Zangram*. Then answer the questions about it.

(10 marks)

1   When the Logan family woke up, they discovered they were in a huge glass dome. They were unaware, however, of the battery of tests and examinations that the Zangrams had carried out on them over a period of several days.

5   Outside the dome, a crowd of Zangrams watched the family through one-way glass. A notice outside the dome said, when translated into English, "On loan from Planet 264S/36 for 30 days". Of course, the Logans knew nothing of this. They believed that somehow they had been kidnapped.

   "Well, at least we're alive," said Mrs Logan, trying to console her
10 children. "Sooner or later, we'll find out where we are and why we're here."

   She was right. They found out the next day when the Zangrams had finally solved the riddle of Earth language and began to communicate with them.

1   What happened to the Logan family before they were put on display? *(2 marks)*

   _____

2   Why does the writer start a new paragraph in three places after the first paragraph? Give a reason why each of the three paragraphs has been started. *(3 marks)*

   _____

   _____

   _____

3   How does the phrase that begins the second paragraph link it to the first paragraph? *(2 marks)*

   _____

4   What does the pronoun "this" in line 8 refer to? *(1 mark)*

_____

5   How does the writer create a dramatic effect at the beginning of the last paragraph? *(2 marks)*

_____

Zangram: extract 3

Now read extract 3 and answer the questions about it. *(10 marks)*

> 1   When the Logans woke up in the car park at Stonehenge, they were puzzled to find their car turned round. They knew something odd had happened, but what? They drove on to Cornwall in some confusion. Their bewilderment deepened when they finally reached the home of Jack's brother and rang the
> 5   doorbell. Tony Logan opened the door and stared at them in a mixture of astonishment and horror.
>   "Where have you been?" he said at last. "We were expecting you a month ago! We checked with your neighbours. We even informed the police because …"
> 10   "A month ago!" echoed Jack Logan. "We agreed July 10th and here we are."
>   Tony stared at his brother, trying to decide whether he was joking or not. "But today is August 10th," he pointed out. "Anyway, come in. You're welcome at any time – even when you're officially 'missing, presumed dead'."
>   Mrs Logan and the children went in. Jack went back to the car to unpack
> 15   the luggage. What he saw in the boot proved that something very strange had occurred.

1   What is similar about the ways in which extracts 1, 2 and 3 end? *(2 marks)*

_____

2   "We even informed the police because …" Why does the author insert …? *(1 mark)*

_____

3   Find five *different* uses of capital letters in the extract. *(5 marks)*

_____

_____

4   Write a sentence saying what Mr Logan found in the boot. *(2 marks)*

_____

unit 17

Describing past events

Key idea

The purpose of writing a recount is to tell about a past event. Recount texts have some common structural and language features that help to identify them.

Time connectives

Read the account of a football match below. Put in ten different linking words or expressions. Choose from those below. *(10 marks)*

right up to the final whistle	shortly afterwards	at the start of the game
within the first ten minutes	ten minutes later	for the rest of the first half
during the half-time break	at half-time	ten minutes from the end
	immediately	

(1)_____ yesterday, Newtown were confidently expected to beat Oldtown by at least two goals. Newtown forced two corners (2)_____, but failed to score. Oldtown struck back but Jordan's shot was wide. (3)_____, Ken Teale put Newtown one up when he headed home a cross from Ojuro. Play was restricted to the centre of the field (4)_____ with Newtown slightly superior. (5)_____ the score remained Newtown 1 – Oldtown 0

   Newtown manager, Joe Kellick, gave his men a pep-talk (6)_____. The players responded with raids on the Oldtown goal, during which Ken Teale scored his second goal. (7)_____ Oldtown veteran, Paul Cranston, scored for Oldtown. Stung by this unexpected goal, Newtown launched another series of attacks (8)_____ and were rewarded when Ojuro scored Newtown's third goal.

   (9)_____ Tom Baxter shot wide for Oldtown. Defences dominated the game (10)_____.

Final score: Newtown 3 – Oldtown 1

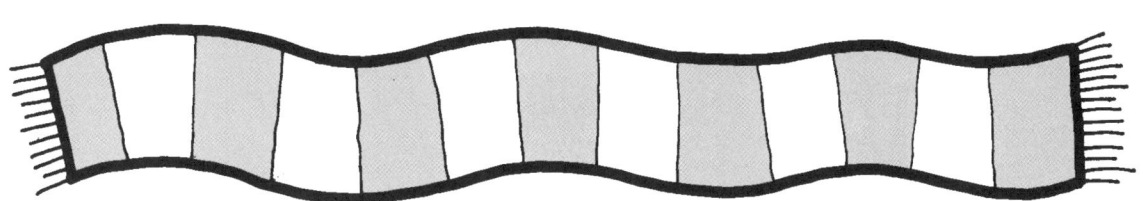

Exploring language

Read 'Hot water' and then answer the questions about it. *(20 marks)*

Hot water

1   Sue went to visit her grandfather, aged 90, in a remote rural district. Grandad cooked a very tasty lunch. However, when Sue put the plates and cutlery on the table, she noticed some tiny brown specks on her plate. She studied the plate thoughtfully for a few moments.

5   "Grandad," she asked hesitantly. "Are you … Are these plates clean?"

"Of course they are," Grandad replied quickly. "They're as clean as hot water can get them. That's for sure. Enjoy your meal and don't worry about the plates."

In the evening, Sue helped Grandad to prepare supper. She was hungry and
10 was just about to put the food on the plates when she saw a thin piece of something on one of the plates. It looked like scrambled egg.

"Grandad," she said firmly. "Are you absolutely sure these plates are clean?"

"No doubt about it," Grandad said with a smile. "They're as clean as hot
15 water can make them. I can guarantee that."

A few minutes later, a neighbour approached Grandad's house. Immediately his dog started to bark furiously. Grandad shouted angrily at the dog, "Cut that out, Hotwater! No more barking! Go and lay down! It's only Jim. You know him."

20 "I call her 'Hotwater'," Grandad explained to Sue, "because she always gets me into trouble."

"Ugh!" Sue thought. "I wonder if … I think I've been had."

"Grandad," she said quietly, "I'll wash the dishes tonight."

34

1   a) Underline any ten adjectives in the passage. *(5 marks)*

    b) Choose six of the adjectives and give words opposite in meaning to them. *(3 marks)*

    _____   _____

    _____   _____

    _____   _____

2   Choose three verbs used in the past tense in the passage. Write them down and then write the present and future tenses of each. *(3 marks)*

    _____

    _____

    _____

3   At the end of the third sentence, what one word can we insert after "plate" to turn the following sentence into a subordinate clause?_____ *(1 mark)*

4   Suggest a reason why Sue was hesitant when she first asked Grandad if the plates were clean? *(1 mark)*

    _____

5   Complete the sentence. *(1 mark)*

    "In line 6, the writer uses 'as … as' to_____

6   a) Write down any six adverbs in the passage. *(3 marks)*

    _____   _____

    _____   _____

    _____   _____

    b) Choose any four of the adverbs and write down words opposite in meaning to them. *(2 marks)*

7   What did Sue mean when she said, "I think I've been had"? *(1 mark)*

    _____

35

Unit 18 Giving instructions

Key idea

Instructions, directions and descriptions of procedures all have to be written clearly and concisely so they are easy to follow. Features such as sequenced and numbered steps, imperative verbs and sequencing connectives are common to this type of writing.

Checklist

Paul wrote the following checklist for maintaining his bike. Read it and then answer the questions about it. *(15 marks)*

> Checklist for maintaining bicycles
> 1 Check brake cables. Do brake blocks make good contact with rims of wheels?
> 2 Is bell fastened firmly? Does it work properly?
> 3 Check if front and rear lights. Replace battry or check dynamo if necessary.
> 4 Chain - tighten and see if any oil is needed.
> 5 Saddle - make sure it is at the right height and comfortable.
> 6 Carrier - check that nuts holding carrier are not lose. Tighten?
> 7 Check nuts holding wheels in place. Tighten or replace if necessary.
> 8 Check air in tyres; check for slow punctures.
> 9 Grease or oil any points that need lubricating, e.g. wheel axils.
> 10 Check that tyre valves are working properly.
> 11 Buy padlock with at least two keys. Get extra keys cut?

1 In step 2, are "firmly" and "properly" adjectives or adverbs?
   _____ *(2 marks)*

2 In step 3, what words are missing from the first sentence?
   _____ *(2 marks)*

3 How could Paul do step 5? _____ *(2 marks)*

4 Find four misspelt words and correct them. *(4 marks)*

   _____   _____

   _____   _____

5 Rewrite step 2 as a single statement with an imperative verb. *(2 marks)*

   _____

36

6   Which two steps could you combine so that there are only ten steps? *(2 marks)*

_____

7   What is the purpose of step 11? *(1 mark)*

_____

Defrosting a freezer

Rewrite Gran's instructions for how to defrost a freezer. Set them out in the right order using no more than ten steps. Leave out points that are not necessary.
(15 marks)

> Well, of course, you have to make sure that you don't make a mess in the kitchen. We don't want any water left on the floor to make the place slippery. That's how Grandad broke a leg a few years ago. Get a few old towels (there are plenty at the bottom of the airing-cupboard) and take them to the freezer. Oh, yes, you'll need a pail or a saucepan to put the water in. Put one of the towels on the floor in front of the freezer to catch the drips. Now, where was I? Ah, yes, empty the freezer. There are only a couple of packets in it now. Stick them in the fridge. Turn off the electricity. Open the freezer wide. Put a couple of towels inside to soak up the water. If you're in a hurry, put a bowl of hot water on a shelf in the freezer. It will help to thaw out the ice. You can poke any pieces of ice free if you like but it's not necessary.
>
> Leave the freezer door open and just be patient. When the ice has all gone, wring out the towels. Clean and dry the freezer. Get rid of any water. Then put the packets back in the freezer and turn it on. Easy!

unit 19 Writing reports

Key idea

Report texts present information on a subject. They describe things as they are. They often feature present-tense verbs, descriptive adjectives and adverbs, and headings and subheadings.

The breakfast report

(10 marks)

1. "Write a report about breakfast in your family," said the teacher to Paul's class. If you were in the class, how would you arrange your ideas? Think of headings for three paragraphs. *(3 marks)*

   _____
   _____
   _____

> Breakfast by Paul
> We have three different kinds of breakfast, classified according to how it is eaten.
> My favourite is a "sitting-down" breakfast. It is a leisurely event on Saturday and Sunday because I do not have to get up early. It includes cereal, fried eggs, beans, mushrooms, toast and jam and a big glass of orange juice.
> A "standing-up" breakfast involves a drink, toast and a piece of fruit. I usually have this on school days because I have less time.
> When I forget to set the alarm and am late for school, I have to have an "on-the-move" breakfast. I shoot out of the house, buy a chocolate bar and eat it before the bell rings.

2. Write paragraph headings for Paul's report above. *(3 marks)*

   _____
   _____
   _____

3. What part of speech is each of these words as it is used in Paul's report? *(4 marks)*
   a) classified _____   b) leisurely _____
   c) usually _____   d) shoot _____

38

The rodent report

This is part of a report on squirrels, written by Sally, age 11 Read it and then answer the questions about it. *(10 marks)*

Grey squirrels

Where they came from

Grey squirrels were brought to Britain from America many years ago and kept in zoos. Some excaped and spread to both rural and urban areas. They have now driven red squirrels away.

_____

They prefer to eat seeds, berries and especially nuts, so they can often be found near oak, beech and other nut trees. However, they also eat birds' eggs and baby birds. Therefore, the presents of squirrels often leads to the absence of birds since they cannot nest safely.

How they behave

Grey squirrels are active during the day and do not hibernate in winter. They are naturaly shy, but not when it comes to food. In some towns, squirrels in parks are so tame that they will take peanuts, if offered, from people's hands.

The problems they cause

Grey squirrels (in fact, all kinds of squirrels) can be pests. They raid berries and other fruit from bushes and trees in poeple's gardens. They also gnaw and eat bark, which leads to the death of trees.

---

1 a) Circle the passive verb in the first paragraph. *(1 mark)*
   b) Why is the verb not active? *(1 mark)* _____

2 Fill in the missing subheading for the second paragraph. *(2 marks)*

3 Draw a box around each of the connectives in the second paragraph. (Do not include "and".) *(2 marks)*

4 Find the four misspelled words in the report. Draw a line through each one and write the correctly spelled word above. *(2 marks)*

5 In the last sentence of the third paragraph, underline the main clause once and the subordinate clause twice. *(2 marks)*

Write a worm report

(10 marks)

Here are some notes about worms.
1 Think of four different headings under which you could group the notes.
2 Then write a four-paragraph report using the notes.

- Do not like light
- Eat dead leaves and soil
- Has complete digestive system
- Help plants to grow
- Live underground
- Long, soft bodies with head and tail end
- Make tunnels to move about
- No bones, eyes, legs
- Soil leaves body making worm "casts"
- Useful creatures – tunnels bring air to soil
- Use muscles and hairs on skin to move
- Take nutrients from soil as it passes through body

WORMS

Paragraph 1 heading:_____

Paragraph 2 heading:_____

Paragraph 3 heading:_____

Paragraph 4 heading:_____

Unit 20 — Persuasive writing

Key idea

Persuasive writing aims to influence the reader towards a particular opinion. It often uses emotional words, figurative devices and imperative verbs.

Email scam

Mrs Stone received this email, which is full of mistakes. Fortunately, she knew it was not from her bank at all, but an attempt by someone to find out her details illegally. Read it and answer the questions. *(10 marks)*

```
Subject: Confirm your details to avoid immediate cancellation to your
account.

Yesterday the bank have a failure of its software this resulted in a
lost of customer data. To help you to avoid from fraud, kindly connect
with the link below to confirm your account registration data, this is
obligatory to protect your account.

Please do not answer to this message. Fill in the form "Confirmation
of Acount Details".
```

1. Which words in the "subject" are meant to frighten the receiver? *(1 mark)*

2. Find an incorrect verb tense. Explain why it is wrong and correct it. *(2 marks)*

3. Find two places where punctuation is wrong or missing. Correct them. *(2 marks)*

4. Find and correct four expressions in which prepositions are used wrongly. *(2 marks)*

5. Find and correct two spelling mistakes. *(2 marks)*

6. Why does the sender of the email put in the sentence, "This is obligatory to protect your account"? *(1 mark)*

The mighty T-watch is here: hep, handy, helpful!

It's COOL and it could be yours!

On one side, it's a watch.
No need to look at it.

Press the button and it tells you the time. Now that's really something – but there's more!

On the other side? A nifty recorder. Up to 10 minutes talktime. No need to take notes.

**Move up to the in-crowd!
ORDER NOW
before they're all snapped up.**

"I love it!" says pop star Kati Lane.

Football legend, Mike O'Shea: "I wouldn't be without mine!"

An advertisement

Read the advertisement above and then answer these questions. *(10 marks)*

1. Which slang words in the advertisment mean "up-to-date, fashionable"? *(1 mark)*

2. What figurative device is used in the second line? *(1 mark)*

3. Why is "COOL" put in capital letters? *(1 mark)*

4. "On the other side? A nifty recorder." Explain why the writer doesn't use complete sentences. *(2 marks)*

5. Why does the advertiser use the word "nifty" instead of "clever"? *(1 mark)*

6. Explain the purpose of the pictures. *(2 marks)*

7. Give one example each of two different verb forms used in the advertisement. *(1 mark)*

8. In the first draft of this advertisement, the advertiser wrote : "Keep up with the in-crowd". Why did she change this to "Move up to the in-crowd"? *(1 mark)*

Getting involved

Miss Benson's class wrote to their local council following three traffic accidents near their school. Read their first draft below and then answer the questions.
(10 marks)

> In the passed six months, there have been three horrific traffic acidents near our school, each time somebody was knocked down by a speeding motorist. We beg the Council to do something to make Bridge Street safer.
>
> We would like to recommend four crucial measures. First of all, we hope the Council can put some speed bumps in the road to slow down traffic. Secondly, we need a pedestran crossing outside our school. Thirdly, it would be a good idea to errect warning sines at each end of Bridge Street, finally, we think that cars should not be aloud to park outside our school for longer than 15 minutes during 8–9 a.m. and 3–4 p.m. on school days.

1 Why do the children mention accidents in their letter? *(1 mark)*

2 Give two examples of powerful, emotive words in the letter. Why do the children use them? *(2 marks)*

3 Find and correct six spelling mistakes in the draft letter. *(3 marks)*

4 Find two places where a comma should be replaced by a full stop. *(1 mark)*

5 Find a passive verb in the first paragraph. *(1 mark)*

6 List the sequencing connectives used in the second paragraph. *(1 mark)*

7 How might the children revise the layout of the second paragraph so that their suggestions are clearer? *(1 mark)*

Unit 21 Writing discussion texts

Key idea

Discussion texts give a balanced presentation of all the various positions that are held about an issue or topic – for example, both sides of an argument.

Television: points of view

"Does television do more harm than good?" Read the first draft of what one pupil wrote and then answer the questions about it. *(10 marks)*

1 Most television shows have a bad influence to viewers, especially young ones. They use swear words and bad language most of the time. Violence is common in "soaps" and are regarded as a model or example to teenagers.

   On the other hand, documentries are both educational and intresting. There is always
5 something new for viewers to learn as long as they can stay awake. Oddly enough, the cartoons are usually OK. They are always amusing without setting a bad example. Sports programmes are also worth watching and do not cause no harm or offence.

   Maybe the only fair answer to the question is that the affect of TV depends upon the individual. If you have firm principals, you can always chose wisely. I hope that television
10 channels will clean up their act, but I won't hold my breathe waiting for that to happen.

1 What more accurate word should the writer use instead of "most" in lines 1 and 2? *(1 mark)*

2 In lines 1 and 3, replace "to" with correct prepositions. *(2 marks)*

3 Explain and correct the error of agreement in the third sentence. *(1 mark)*

4 Explain and correct the error in the last sentence of the second paragraph. *(1 mark)*

5 Correct six spelling mistakes in the last two paragraphs. *(3 marks)*

6 Is the writer's discussion well-balanced? Explain your answer. *(2 marks)*

Maths – or no maths?

"Should children be allowed to decide whether they want to study maths or not?" Read the first draft of what one pupil wrote and then answer the questions about it. *(10 marks)*

1   Some people say that we do not need maths in our daily lifes because calculaters and computers can give us all the answers. I don't agree to that because sometimes if we don't know any maths it is easy for crooks to cheat us. Also we need maths whenever we buy or sell anything and maybe we have no calculator available.

5   On the other hand, it is true that algebra and geometry can be too difficult to some children and they become confused and fed up. Then they may even hate the subject and start to behave badly at school. Perhaps the right thing to do is to make basic maths compulsery up to, say, the age of 14 and to make it optional after that. If somebody is no good at maths (even when he or she tries very hard), it is a waist of time to force the

10 person to continue to study the subject.

1   Find and correct four spelling errors: two in each paragraph *(2 marks)*

2   Correct the mistakes in the use of prepositions in lines 2 and 5 *(1 mark)*

3   What more formal words could the writer use instead of "crooks" (line 3) and "fed up" (line 6)? *(1 mark)*

4   How many points for each side of the argument does the writer give? What are they? *(4 marks)*

5   Do you agree with the writer's conclusion? Give reasons for your answer. *(2 marks)*

Should it be a crime to kill any wild animal?

(10 marks)

Put a suitable word in each blank space. *(7 marks – 0.5 mark for each correct answer)*

I am in favour of protecting wild animals, but there (1)_____ two main reasons (2)_____ I do not think it (3)_____ be a crime to kill any wild animal. Firstly, sometimes it is (4)_____ to kill wild animals such as mice, rats and rabbits. (5)_____ we do not kill some of them, they will increase (6)_____ cause serious problems. A (7)_____ reason is that sometimes wild animals, such (8)_____ boars, foxes, badgers and deer, increase and (9)_____ a threat to farmers. Then it is necessary to kill some of (10)_____.

We must also remember (11)_____ some farmers keep cattle, sheep, deer, goats and (12)_____ animals for their milk or meat. Are these wild animals? If somebody kills a wild pony on Dartmoor (13)_____ that a crime? As I said earlier, I think some wild animals should be protected, but making it a crime to kill one is not the (14)_____ way of doing it.

- Do you think it should be a crime to kill wild animals? Give two reasons for your answer. *(3 marks)*

_____
_____
_____
_____
_____

Investigating English expressions

 **Key idea** ....

Investigating language is the best way to find out how it works.

American English ....

(16 marks)

Americans speak English, but many of their words differ from British English. Do you know what they're talking about? Put the right British word by each American word below. *(8 marks – 0.5 mark for each correct answer)*

> taxi   pavement   sweets   dummy (for a baby)   nappy   trousers
> autumn   boot (of a car)   lorry   curtains   petrol   sweet biscuits
> lift   handbag   queue   tap (for water)

1 cab _____

2 line _____

3 fall _____

4 truck _____

5 diaper _____

6 purse _____

7 candy _____

8 pants _____

9 trunk (of a car) _____

10 gas(oline) _____

11 pacifier _____

12 cookies _____

13 faucet _____

14 sidewalk _____

15 drapes _____

16 elevator _____

Now find out for yourself the British words for these American words. *(8 marks)*

17 drugstore _____

18 closet _____

19 stove _____

20 hood (of a car) _____

21 vacation _____

22 garbage _____

23 movies _____

24 buck (money) _____

Investigating idioms

Put the right idiom on each line below. *(14 marks)*

- a Tartar
- eyewash
- a close shave
- a mouthpiece
- a square peg in a round hole
- a rough diamond
- a pig in a poke
- a fool's paradise
- a blank cheque
- a fly in the ointment
- a red herring
- a hornets' nest
- soft soap
- a white lie

1   A _____ is an untrue statement which is made for good reasons, for example to protect an innocent person.

2   _____ is something (usually a statement) meant to deceive people or hide something wrong.

3   _____ is a person who is very difficult to deal with even if you have some advantage over them. Many years ago, if you captured this person in a battle, he would prove a troublesome prisoner.

4   _____ is something which is meant to deceive you, perhaps by making you look in the wrong direction when trying to solve a problem.

5   _____ is permission to do as you like, for example to spend as much money as you like because the cheque has been signed but no amount has been put in.

6   If you spend a lot of time dreaming about winning a lottery, you may live in _____, thinking about something nice which will never happen.

7   If you buy _____, you buy something (such as a pig tied up in a sack) before you have had a chance to inspect it.

8   _____ is flattery.

9   _____ is somebody who appears tough or lacking in manners, but is really very kind and generous.

10 If a person is in a job that does not suit him or her, we may say that the person is _____.

11 _____ is an obstacle to a plan.

12 Sometimes we call a narrow escape _____.

13 _____ is somebody who speaks on behalf of another person or organisation, often to give excuses or reasons for an action.

14 _____ is a source of possible trouble because if you interfere you may create a worse situation.

Key Grammar is a brand new resource, specifically planned to cover all the key grammar objectives in self-contained units of work. The pupil books feature:

- clear, progressive units covering all key learning objectives
- plenty of practice and consolidation work
- opportunities to challenge and extend children's learning
- a clear mark scheme
- exercises in an appropriate context, with engaging illustrations

The workbooks provide activities for additional practice, differentiation, and homework. The important language skills coverage in **Key Grammar** is complemented by two associated series: **Key Comprehension** and **Key Spelling** – up-to-date and engaging resources which reinforce key teaching points and enable children to practise, consolidate and extend their learning. For further information about **Key Comprehension** and **Key Spelling** call our Customer Services Department on **(+44) (0)1865 888000**.

Author: Alan Etherton

Ginn is an imprint of Pearson education Limited, a company incorporated in England and Wales, having its registered office at Edinburgh Gate, Harlow, Essex, CM20 2JE.
Registered company number: 872828

www.ginn.co.uk
Help and support for teachers plus the widest range of education solutions

© Harcourt Education Limited 2005

This book is copyright and reproduction of the whole or part without the publishers' written permission is prohibited.

Key Grammar Workbook 4
ISBN: 978 0602 20685 7
Level 4 Easy Order Pack: 978 0602 20651 2
Level 4 Workbook 6 Pack: 978 0602 20648 2

First published 2005

16
13

Cover illustration by Pet Gotohda
Cover design by Tom Cole
Designed by Nicki Wise, Te Marama Design
Illustrations by David Semple, Gary Swift, Andrew Painter

Printed and bound in China (GCC/13)

# Grammar Workbook 4

Contents

Unit 1	Word classes	page 2
Unit 2	Using standard English	page 4
Unit 3	Active and passive verbs 1	page 6
Unit 4	Connectives	page 8
Unit 5	Forming complex sentences 1	page 10
Unit 6	Punctuation	page 12
Unit 8	Active and passive verbs 2	page 14
Unit 9	Official language	page 16
Unit 10	Forming complex sentences 2	page 18
Unit 11	Making notes	page 20
Unit 12	Writing a summary	page 22
Unit 13	Editing	page 24
Unit 14	Conditional sentences	page 27
Unit 16	Narrative writing	page 30
Unit 17	Describing past events	page 33
Unit 18	Giving instructions	page 36
Unit 19	Writing reports	page 38
Unit 20	Persuasive writing	page 41
Unit 21	Writing discussion texts	page 44
Unit 22	Investigating English expressions	page 47

Unit 1 — Word classes

🔑 Key idea

Words are categorised in classes according to the jobs they do in a sentence: noun, pronoun, verb, adjective, adverb, preposition, conjunction and interjection. Words can belong to more than one class.

Work it out

Give one-word answers. *(10 marks)*

1 Which proper noun is the name of the Italian capital? _____
2 Which adjective is the opposite of "wise"? _____
3 Which collective noun means "a lot of (birds flying) together"? _____
4 Which verb means "to tremble with cold or fear"? _____
5 Which pronoun is the opposite of "no one"? _____
6 Which proper noun is the name of the shortest month of the year? _____
7 Which adverb is the opposite of "rarely"? _____
8 What is the second part of the conjunction "not only…"? _____
9 What adverb can we form from "skill"? _____
10 Which verb means to "make longer"? _____

Which word?

Ring or underline the right word in the brackets. *(10 marks)*

1 It was dark, so we couldn't see (nothing, anything) clearly.
2 Would you mind (to wait, waiting) a few minutes?
3 There (are, is) more than one way of solving this problem.
4 Where (are, is) the rest of the players?
5 The change in the plan will not have a great deal of (affect, effect) on us.
6 Don't be so (impatience, impatient), John!
7 Between you and (I, me), I think Margaret is quite right to be suspicious.
8 This photo is different (than, from) that one.
9 We watched the marathon, but we did not (took, take) part in it.
10 Your new bike is much better than (Paul's, Pauls').

Classify it

Read this passage from *Nicholas Nickleby* by Charles Dickens. Place each of the underlined words under the correct heading in the grid below. *(10 marks – 0.5 mark for each correctly placed word)*

Dotheboy's Hall <u>was</u> not a hall at all, <u>but</u> a bare and dirty room with a <u>couple</u> of windows, in which most of the glass was broken. There were a few old <u>rickety</u> desks, <u>cut</u> and notched, and inked and damaged, in <u>every</u> possible way; a detached desk for <u>Squeers</u>; and another <u>for</u> his assistant. The ceiling was supported, like <u>that</u> of a barn, by cross beams and rafters; and the walls were so stained that it was impossible to tell <u>whether</u> they had ever been painted or whitewashed.

But the pupils! How his last hopes <u>faded</u> as <u>he</u> looked <u>around</u>! Pale and haggard faces of old men, boys of stunted growth, and others whose long thin legs would <u>hardly</u> carry their <u>stooping</u> bodies, all <u>crowded</u> together; there were the bleary eye, the hare-lip, the crooked foot, and every problem arising from <u>cruelty</u> and neglect. There were little faces which should have been handsome, darkened with the scowl of suffering; there were vicious-faced boys, brooding like prisoners in jail; <u>and</u> there were children <u>who</u> were weeping <u>with</u> loneliness…

nouns	
pronouns	
verbs	
adjectives	
adverbs	
prepositions	
conjunctions	

Using standard English

Key idea

We can use non-standard English in speech, but we must use standard English in formal written work.

Does it agree?

Underline the subject each time. (It may be a single word or a group of words.) Then circle the right word in the brackets so that the verb agrees with its subject.
(14 marks)

1 How much of the information in newspaper reports or radio and television news reports (are, is) completely accurate?

2 According to a report on television, a reward of several thousand pounds (has, have) been offered for information leading to the arrest of the robbers.

3 The driver of the bus – together with two of the passengers – (was, were) slightly injured in the accident.

4 (Is, Are) there any mud on your shoes?

5 The number of flights from London to Spain (have, has) risen in recent years because more people like to spend a holiday on the Spanish coast.

6 There (is, are) a number of reasons why people prefer to spend their holiday abroad. The main attraction is the better climate overseas.

7 What a nuisance! All the traffic (has, have) stopped. There must have been an accident somewhere ahead of us.

8 Before the play started, a member of the cast peeped through the curtains and said, "Oh, good! The audience (is, are) a really big one tonight. There are no empty seats."

9 Everybody in our class (want, wants) to join in the picnic, don't they?

10 How long (has, have) all this rubbish been lying here?

11 As a result of a change in the law, the poor (is, are) likely to be better off.

12 A good standard of numeracy (is, are) necessary in many jobs.

13 At least a third of those players (is, are) from foreign countries.

14 The majority of the pupils in our class (does, do) not come to school in a car.

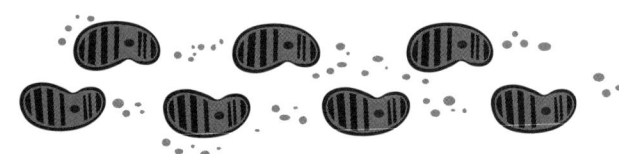

Choose the right word

Ring or underline the right words in the brackets. *(8 marks)*

1 This shop doesn't sell cosmetics (or, nor) health foods.

2 My sister doesn't like garlic and (so, nor) do I.

3 Sometimes people are not sure where to keep their money. If they hide (them, it) at home, there is always a risk of burglary.

4 The manager told his staff that he hadn't (no, any) intention of resigning.

5 John did not feel very well at the start of the cross-country race, and he felt much (worse, worser) at the end.

6 After the show, my friend and (me, I) bought some chips and ate (it, them) on the way home.

7 We need somebody to check all the electrical (equipment, equipments) before we turn on the computer and heating.

8 Our visit to Scandinavia (maybe, may be) described as a tour rather than a holiday.

Make it formal

Write more formal expressions that we can use instead of the italic words. *(8 marks)*

1 That's a *lousy* idea. _____

2 There's a rumour that their business is *on the rocks*. _____

3 All the *kids* in my class agree with me. _____

4 I haven't got *nothing* special to tell you. _____

5 The man said he didn't know *no one* with that name. _____

6 The fact that he is guilty *sticks out like a sore thumb*. _____

7 This hairstyle is gradually *catching on*. _____

8 *How come* you're not at school today? _____

Unit 3

Active and passive verbs 1

🔑 Key idea

Verbs can be in the **active** or **passive** voice.

A dangerous job

Write in the *passive* Simple Present form of the verbs in brackets. *(12 marks)*

In Malaysia, rubber (1) _____ (grow) on many estates. At dawn, rubber-tappers start work. Many of them are women and they know that their work can be dangerous. Sometimes tappers (2) _____ (attack) by a tiger. When they bend down to tap a tree, they (3) _____ (sometimes mistake) for a wild animal and attacked by a hungry tiger.

Tappers start work before the sun rises. First, a cut (4) _____ (make) in a mature tree. A tin or half a coconut shell (5) _____ (fasten) to the tree. It (6) _____ (use) to collect latex from the cut. The tapper cuts many trees. Then he or she returns to the first tree. Latex in the tin (7) _____ (empty) into a pail which (8) _____ (take) to the small "factory" on the estate. Chemicals (9) _____ (add) to the latex and mixed in well. Later on, the latex (10) _____ (squeeze) into sheets which (11) _____ (hang) in a smoke-filled hut. Finally, the sheets of rubber (12) _____ (tie) up in bales, ready for export to other countries.

A gas leak

Put in the *passive* form of the verbs in brackets. Use *has/have been + a past participle* each time. *(10 marks)*

One evening Mrs Wilson (Mrs W) was on her way home from work. She got off a bus and started to walk the 200 metres to her home. As she walked round a corner, she was surprised to see a crowd of people outside a wrecked house. There were fire-engines and police cars there too. Mrs Wilson's friend, Mrs Johnson (Mrs J), was in the crowd.

Mrs W: What's the matter? What's happened?

Mrs J: There was a gas leak. That house (1) _____ (wreck) completely.

Mrs W: (2) _____ anybody _____ (injure)?

Mrs J: Yes, two people (3)_____(hurt). They (4)_____ (take) to hospital already.

Mrs W: What are the fire-engines doing here?

Mrs J: There was a small fire but it (5)_____ (bring) under control. The gas company (6)_____ (inform), so men are coming to repair the pipe. A lot of debris (7)_____ (hurl) across the road, so the windows in those houses (8)_____ (break). The people in those houses (9)_____ (evacuate). There were some elderly people in that old folks' home over there. They (10) _____ (move) to another home temporarily.

Mrs W: Is there anything we can do to help?

Mrs J: No, I don't think so.

In trouble

Put in the *passive* future form of the verbs in brackets. Use *will be* + *a past participle*. *(8 marks)*

Paul's friend, Mike, was sent off during a football match for hitting an opponent. Now Paul is asking his dad, a referee, what will happen to Mike.

Paul: Will Mike get into trouble?

Dad: Yes, I'm afraid he will. I'm sure he (1)_____ (charge) with hitting an opponent. Then he (2)_____ (ask) to attend a hearing before the Disciplinary Committee. He (3)_____ (tell) what he is charged with.

Paul: What will happen after that?

Dad: He (4)_____ (give) a chance to listen to the referee's report and ask any questions. Then he (5)_____ (invite) to make his statement and admit the charge or try to deny it.

Paul: I don't think he will deny it because everybody saw what happened. What will the Committee do?

Dad: Well, Mike (6)_____ (inform) of the decision in writing. It is probable that he (7)_____ (ban) for a few months. If he has a bad record, he (8)_____ (fine) as well, I should think.

Unit 4 Connectives

Key idea

Connectives are words and phrases that are used to link different parts of a text. They can join words, phrases, clauses, sentences and paragraphs.

Types of connectives

Underline the connectives in the sentences below. Then put them under the correct heading in the grid. *(10 marks)*

1. Paul decided to buy the bicycle although it was expensive.
2. We can go out when the rain stops.
3. Mary stuck a stamp on the envelope and then she posted the invitation.
4. Following my operation, I developed an infection in the wound.
5. We can go for a picnic on Saturday if the weather is good.
6. Mike can't go out to play now because he hasn't finished his homework yet.
7. You can go to London by train or you can travel on the express bus.
8. Our new house is bigger than our old one. Moreover, it has a large garden.
9. Most people like Susan, but I think she is rather conceited.
10. Despite having a terrible cold, the soprano performed her solo.

Addition	Time	Cause and effect	Opposition

Connective starters

Complete each sentence in a suitable way to show that you understand the connective. *(10 marks)*

1 We'll have to wait here until _____

2 If you eat too much, _____

3 We couldn't move the wardrobe because _____

4 Although it snowed last night, _____

5 In spite of the cold weather, _____

6 Kate is very fond of animals, so _____

7 Choose your sweets and then _____

8 I forgot to set the alarm. As a result, _____

9 The game started on time despite _____

10 I often eat fish. However, _____

Choosing connectives

Ring or underline the right word in the brackets. *(10 marks)*

1 We can go there by taxi. (Alternately, Alternatively) we can take the bus.

2 (Despite, In spite) the discount, Mrs Lee decided not to buy the car.

3 We had to leave our house when a pipe burst. Now we're waiting for the workmen to complete the repairs. In the (while, meantime), we're staying with my grandparents.

4 The team has succeeded because the owner of the club is a billionaire. (Nevertheless, Furthermore) it has one of the best managers in Europe.

5 Crocodiles have no predators to attack them. (Consequently, Subsequently) they manage to live for many years.

6 Trees can spread their seeds in many ways. (Meanwhile, For example,) sycamore seeds have "wings" to help them fly away from the parent tree.

7 We don't agree with Paul's plan. On the (other hand, contrary), we think it could be disastrous for the club.

8 His plan contains several faults. (Nevertheless, Similarly) it contains some good points.

9 You ought to buy yourself a watch (instead of, in spite of) borrowing mine.

10 Most shops have security cameras (providing, so that) they can catch thieves.

Unit 5: Forming complex sentences 1

Key idea

Complex sentences are made up of more than one clause. The clauses can be joined in different ways.

Completing sentences

Complete these sentences in any sensible way. Draw a ring round the connecting words. *(10 marks)*

1 A library is a place where _____

2 There was a hidden cottage where_____

3 Don't forget to turn the lights off when _____

4 People go to a dentist when _____

5 Plants will usually grow well if _____

6 Traffic police may stop a motorist if _____

7 Mary had the flu last week, so _____

8 Paul could not hear what people were saying on television, so _____
_____

9 You can go to your friend's house now, provided that _____
_____

10 You can borrow my bike if you like, provided that _____
_____

What and where?

Complete each sentence by saying *what* people are doing and *where* they are doing it. Start with a present participle (an –ing word) *(10 marks)*

   Example: We watched some men **repairing** a pipe in the road near our home.

1 Ashra heard two women _____

2 When I came out of my house, I noticed a man _____
_____

3 When we reached the beach, we saw some fishermen _____
_____

4   Before we entered the park, we stopped to watch some boys _____
    _____

5   When Sue looked out of the window, she saw a blackbird _____
    _____

6   Last night on television we watched some girls _____
    _____

7   After a few minutes, the fox came to a field and was happy to see some lambs
    _____

8   Mr Evans woke up during the night when he heard somebody _____
    _____

9   When our bus passed Mary's house, we saw her father _____
    _____

10 The lifeguard ran down the beach when he heard somebody _____
    _____

Punctuating complex sentences

Put in the missing commas. *(10 marks)*

1   Yesterday in broad daylight the police caught two men trying to rob a bank.

2   The frightened rabbit stayed absolutely still hoping that the fox had not seen it.

3   My father the manager of the store starts work before 8 a.m.

4   Last night the temperature in most Welsh towns was above freezing-point. In Aberystwyth however it was minus four degrees.

5   Did you enjoy yourself at the party last Saturday Kate?

6   Although the concert lasted for over two hours the audience was captivated by the soloist who was only ten.

7   Not having seen her cousin for several years Sue was surprised to see how tall he was.

8   Birmingham is a very large city. In fact it is one of the largest in the United Kingdom.

9   When the phone rang Peter hurried to answer it hoping that it was his friend.

10 Leaping over the wall the frightened animal disappeared into the woods.

Unit 6 Punctuation

Key idea

Adding clauses increases the complexity of sentences, so more punctuation is required.

Using commas

Put in commas where necessary. The sentences show various different uses of commas. *(10 marks)*

1 The home of the Duke of Devonshire has 173 rooms and houses more than 60 types of clocks.

2 Paul go and find Mary please.

3 Worms are probably the most common bait for fish. If you expect to catch fish therefore you must be prepared to handle worms.

4 'Ugh! I'm not going to touch a worm' Katie said.

5 One of our neighbours Mrs Collins is a very experienced nurse.

6 Even if I were a billionaire I would not want to live alone in a huge isolated house.

7 Very few people read poetry books in their leisure time. Many modern pop songs however contain their own type of poetry and are very popular.

8 When tadpoles get older their tails get shorter their legs get longer and they gradually develop into very small frogs.

9 Pauline Taylor whose father is a maths teacher is always top of the class in maths not surprisingly.

10 If you're ready it's time for us to leave for the airport Grandad.

Using speech marks

Each of these unpunctuated sentences contains direct speech. Rewrite them, putting in the speech marks and other punctuation marks and capital letters that are necessary. *(10 marks)*

1 My friend said to me would you mind checking this letter for me please

2 I told her you've left an r out of preferred

3 Miss Lee told me you should have written chose and not choose

4 I heard Paul shout out wait for me Mike so we waited for him

5 If you've finished your homework my mother said you can watch the film on TV

6 when the performance ended the audience rose to their feet and shouted bravo

7 clamouring up the treacherous rocks the mountain rescuer cried hold on

8 can i follow you asked grace i dont know the way besides its dark

9 the wizard whose wand was misbehaving shook his finger and said abracadabra

10 louise rubbed her eyes yawned and mumbled whats the matter

More punctuation practice

Put in any necessary punctuation marks and capital letters. *(10 marks)*

1 its the end of march tomorrow remember to put your clocks on an hour

2 remember what people say in america spring forward fall back

3 in sentence 2 the word fall means autumn

4 there are 24 children in our class 14 boys and 10 girls

5 i think that jacket is a real bargain don't you mary

6 that was my first visit to a zoo I thought it was very interesting

7 come in sit down would you like a soft drink

8 some girls like to play netball or rounders others prefer hockey

9 the speaker promised the people many things more jobs higher pay longer holidays and lower taxes

10 don't forget the saying nothing ventured nothing gained

Unit 8 Active and passive verbs 2

🔑 Key idea

Verbs can be in the **active** or **passive** voice.

Look to the future

Read the two passages. Write in the *passive* future form of the verbs in brackets.
(10 marks)

A. Tomorrow part of the motorway (1)_____ (close) for urgent resurfacing. The work (2)_____ (complete) by 4 p.m., when the road (3)_____ (reopen) to traffic. While the road is closed, traffic (4)_____ (divert). Notices (5)_____ (put) up to show motorists the route to follow.

B. Miss Harris told her class, "Our Sports Day will be on next Friday. It (6)_____ (hold) on the school field, starting at noon. All lessons will be (7)_____ (cancel) for the afternoon of that day. All parents (8)_____ (invite) to come. If bad weather is forecast, you (9)_____ (tell) and Sports Day (10)_____ (postpone) to the following week."

Will, may or must?

Read these sentences carefully. Then decide whether to put in *will*, *may* or *must*.
(10 marks)

1. This letter is urgent. It _____ be posted as soon as possible.

2. During a thunderstorm, don't shelter under a tree. It _____ be hit by lightning. If it is hit, you _____ be killed or seriously injured.

3. Be careful if you see an adder. It is a venomous snake with black zigzag marks on its top. Don't go near or touch an adder. If you do, you _____ be bitten. Then you _____ be taken to hospital. You _____ be given an antidote to fight the venom from the snake.

4 Check your bike before you go for a long ride. The brakes _____ be checked and the tyres _____ be pumped up if necessary.

5 When people return from a holiday overseas, their passports _____ be checked by an Immigration Officer. Then their luggage _____ be searched by a Customs Officer.

Active to passive

Change these sentences so that they contain *passive* verbs instead of active ones. Leave out the italic words. *(10 marks)*

1 *Somebody* stole Mr Jackson's car during the night.

2 Before the dentist drilled my tooth, *she* gave me an injection.

3 *Some workmen* pulled down that old factory last week.

4 *The strong wind* blew down two trees last night.

5 *Somebody* has just taken Mrs Sharpe to hospital.

6 *Two dustmen* collect our rubbish every Friday.

7 *People* grow a lot of apples in this part of the country.

8 *Sharks or other large fish* sometimes attack swimmers not far from the beach.

9 *The Mayor* will open the new school tomorrow.

10 *Several workmen* will redecorate our school during the holidays.

# Unit 9

Official language

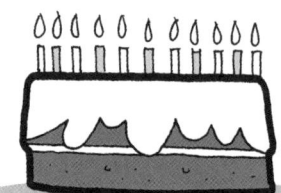

🔑 Key idea

Formal and official documents have certain language features that distinguish them from informal writing.

Informal: first person (personal); colloquial/slang vocabulary; use of contractions; short, simple sentences; exclamations, questions

Formal: third person (impersonal); technical, subject-specific vocabulary; no contractions; complex sentences; statements

> *Len Benton sent his friend, Mary Evans, a fake formal letter from a firm of solicitors when she wanted to borrow his bicycle. Mary decided to continue the game with Len. She sent him this invitation to her birthday party.*
>
> > On behalf of Miss Mary Evans, we have very considerable pleasure in requesting the pleasure of your company at a sumptuous festive social gathering of young attractive females and boisterous males to celebrate the eleventh anniversary of her blessed nativity.
> >
> > Please be informed accordingly that this joyful event will take place at Miss Evans' ancestral place of residence at 462 Rowan Road on Saturday 25 April, commencing punctually at 4 p.m. and drawing to a close by 8 p.m.
> >
> > To enable us to make adequate preparations, we would greatly appreciate it if you would kindly get in touch with us and indicate whether or not you will be able to join all concerned in this celebration. Kindly let us know what you decide before noon on 21 April so that our plans may be finalised well in advance. Alternatively, you may prefer to make your decision known directly to Mary (by phone, email, fax or in person).
> >
> > We are asked to pass on to all guests Mary's particular request that presents should not be brought or sent.

What do they mean?

Find and underline the expressions in Mary's invitation that have these meanings.
(10 marks)

| 1 are happy | 3 party | 5 birthday | 7 home | 9 would like |
| 2 to invite | 4 children | 6 note (verb) | 8 finishing | 10 everybody |

In translation

Len's brother asked him what was in the letter from Mary. Pretend you are Len. Tell your brother – in everyday English – what the main points of the invitation are. *(10 marks)*

_____
_____
_____
_____
_____
_____

Keep it simple

Give the meaning of the expressions in italics. Use ordinary, everyday English that makes the meaning clear but uses fewer words. *(10 marks)*

1 Please *contact him in writing*. _____

2 Write your name here, *giving your surname and all given names*.
_____

3 *In the event that* you are unable to come, bring a note when you recover.
_____

4 Mike missed a lot of lessons at school *as a result* of illness.
_____

5 Ask a parent or *the person who is legally responsible for looking after you* to write a note to your teacher, explaining why you were absent.
_____

6 Peter cannot come today because he is *suffering from some illness*.
_____

7 The *man who has been accused of robbery but has not yet been tried or convicted* will give evidence tomorrow.
_____

8 Mr Macdonald is a farmer, so he would like to *wipe out and completely get rid of* all the rabbits on his farm.
_____

9 Your claim for compensation will be *studied in detail to ascertain all aspects of the problem*.
_____

10 You will be told *what is eventually decided by officials who look into your case*.
_____

Forming complex sentences 2

Key idea

subordinate clause   main clause   subordinate clause

After the party, *we all went straight home* *because it was late*.

There are different types of subordinate clauses. They are linked to the main clause with connectives.

Adding connectives

Put one of the following connectives in each blank space below. *(10 marks)*

if	after	before	although	when	so
while	despite	provided	so	that	

1. I have a poster that reminds me to wash my hands _____ I have a meal, and to clean my teeth _____ I have eaten anything.

2. _____ Mum agrees, we're going to have a barbecue this evening _____ it doesn't rain.

3. The house in Elm Street was too expensive and _____ my parents decided not to buy it _____ we all liked it very much

4. You can borrow these videos but let me have them back _____ Mary can watch them _____ she returns from holiday.

5. The fire started _____ men were carrying out repairs. It destroyed the whole building _____ the efforts of the firemen.

Punctuating complex sentences

Punctuate these sentences correctly. Don't forget to put in capital letters where necessary. *(10 marks – 2 marks for each correct sentence)*

1 we expected toms friend to come at 5 pm however he didnt arrive until 530

2 in the middle of lunch a boy rushed into the canteen shouting fire fire

3 I put my books away and turned off the light then I went to bed

4 when the phone rang maya picked it up expecting to hear her friends voice

5 the answer peter gave although partially correct was not the right one

Joining sentences

Join each group of sentences to make one sentence. You can change, add or omit words. *(10 marks – 2.5 marks for each correct sentence)*

1 The rain stopped. We played in the garden. The grass was still wet. We were quite chilly.

2 The girl won lots of money. She gave half of it to charity. She is Janet's cousin.

3 This is the ring. My aunt gave it to me. I was ten then. It is beautiful.

4 Uncle George is over fifty. He completed the marathon. He raised lots of money for charity.

# Unit 11

Making notes

Key idea

We make notes to extract the most important points from written words (such as information text) or spoken words (such as a telephone conversation or interview). We write them down in a shorter form.

Babysitting

You are babysitting for Mrs Done. You receive some phone calls and need to jot down notes so that you can write out messages for her. Make notes. *(10 marks)*

1. Is that Connie Jackson? Oh, well, maybe I could leave a message for her. My name is Peter Brown. I was going to call on her tomorrow at her office at about ten but something has come up, so I can't make it. Please ask her to phone my secretary at 099-438 tomorrow to fix another appointment. Thursday or Friday would be fine for me, ideally in the morning. Thanks. Goodbye.

2. Can I interest you in a good deal on double-glazing? This week we're offering … Oh, I see. Hmmm. Well, perhaps you'd tell her that Glunk Glass have this special offer next week, for seven days only. We're offering a discount of twenty-five per cent for two windows or more. If further details are needed, ask the lady to phone Andrew Brown at 047-738 any time. Thanks.

Customer services

You are learning the work in the Customer Services Department of a busy store. People phone, so you have to take notes and then tell the manager what the complaint is about. Read what these people said to you. Make notes. *(10 marks)*

1. My name's Ivy Trott. What's that? No, I'm not related to her. What I want to do is complain about the Milky Way Mousse. Don't get me wrong. I like them very much, but you never seem to have any in stock. What's happened? Are the staff eating them all? How come you've never got any on sale? Please ask somebody to order some more, pronto!

2   I want to complain about the tomatoes in your fruit and vegetable section. I usually buy a packet of six. Twice I've found that two of the tomatoes were bad underneath. They look all right on top but when you get them out – that's a different story. Maybe you could have a word with your order clerk or whoever does the ordering and change your supplier. I'll check up on them in the coming weeks and let you know if I see any improvement. I will be bringing back the two bad ones I bought this week and will expect a refund.

Local newspaper reporter

You are a reporter in the office of a local newspaper. You receive these phone calls. Make notes of the important points. *(10 marks)*

1   In the past week, six cars have been damaged by hooligans in Leo's car park. Each of them had a window broken. One had its tyres slashed. Three had the paintwork scratched badly. The damage occurs between about 10 p.m. and 6 a.m. I can tell you the names and addresses of a couple of louts who hang out there if you're interested.

2   You ought to investigate a house in Lufton Road. It's number 39 There's something fishy going on there. It's been empty for about six months, but recently the lights have been on and I've seen a lot of people coming and going with huge boxes at all hours of the day. There are often five or six lorries parked in the road at a time. There's a problem with burglary in our area at the moment. Perhaps the house is being used to store stolen goods.

Unit 12 — Writing a summary

🔑 Key idea

A summary is a re-telling in a shorter number of words of something you have read or heard.
- Summaries require writing in complete sentences.
- Summaries should include the main idea and important points only.

One-word summaries

In each case, give one word that summarises the group of words below. *(10 marks)*

1. a place where water is stored so that it can be sent to homes
   _____

2. walking along slowly and hardly lifting the feet off the ground
   _____

3. a long hole through a hill, often for a railway line
   _____

4. a place where people can keep their money and earn interest
   _____

5. a man or woman who looks after sick or injured people
   _____

6. wet stuff that comes trickling down from the clouds
   _____

7. biting and biting and biting (when the food is tough)
   _____

8. not liking to be delayed or kept waiting for anything
   _____

9. taken into custody (by a police officer)
   _____

10. in a way showing considerable skill
    _____

Headlines

Make up five newspaper headlines (of not more than six words each). *(10 marks – 2 marks for each one)*

1 A mineshaft has opened under a house in a village near Durham, causing half the house to disappear down the shaft. Luckily, the owners were in the other half of the house and were not hurt – but they were shocked.

   _____

2 A large black animal, similar to a panther, has been seen by a farmer in a field near Taunton. Several sheep have been killed in the vicinity recently.

   _____

3 Cricketer Jason Foley has just scored 500 not out in a test match against Australia. He has earned a five-figure bonus for his achievement.

   _____

4 A girl, aged 12, fell at home, hit her head on a stone floor and became unconscious. Her mother dialled 999 but the ambulance did not arrive until an hour later. By that time, the girl was gravely ill. She died shortly after she was taken to hospital. Her parents were outraged and very angry at the delay.

   _____

5 A venomous spider was found in a bunch of grapes imported from South Africa. The purchaser spotted the spider and took it to a laboratory where it was examined and then killed. It was found to be extremely harmful. The store which sold the grapes has apologised and promised to inspect imports more thoroughly.

   _____

What can you remember?

Write a summary of each of the things below. Use a single sentence each time. Do not use more than twenty words in each sentence. *(10 marks – 2.5 marks for each sentence)*

1 A recent lesson which you enjoyed at school _____
   _____

2 What you did yesterday from 5 p.m. until the time you went to bed _____
   _____

3 The last television programme you watched _____
   _____

4 Your favourite book _____
   _____

Editing

Key idea

Editing involves reviewing and improving our own (or someone else's) writing to make it more effective.

Using more effective words

You are editing a composition written by a friend. Suggest two more effective words that could be used instead of the words in italics. Your words do not have to be synonyms of the italic words, but they should be suitable for the situation.

(10 marks – 0.5 mark for each suitable answer)

1 A group of children ran away in front of us. When we were nearly at the corner, a woman *came* out of her house. She was upset and waved her arms angrily at us.

   _____   _____

2 'Go away! Get out of here!' she *said to* us *loudly*.

   _____   _____

   _____   _____

3 The policeman *looked* at us. His face *indicated* that trouble was coming.

   _____   _____

   _____   _____

4 The old man *moved* painfully towards the receptionist.

   _____   _____

5 Mary wore a *nice* outfit to her friend's party.

   _____   _____

6 The tornado *pulled apart* the town, leaving a trail of destruction behind it.

   _____   _____

7 The poor animal *moved* towards us on its three good legs as if *asking* us to help.

   _____   _____

   _____   _____

Correcting errors

The following sentences are taken from a report by a pupil about the school canteen. Edit the sentences by correcting any mistakes in them. Write out the sentences correctly. *(10 marks – 0.5 mark for each correction)*

1 In the coarse of our investigations, we watched pupils had lunch on sevral days.

2 We noticed that some pupil had to queue a long time before they could obtained there food.

3 We therefore suggest that there should be two seperate sessions for lunch, the younger children can eat 20 minutes earlier then the oldest pupils.

4 This will also prevent the food to becoming cold and will enable the servers to work more careful, they are all in favour of this change.

5 We asked each pupil to complete a questionaire about the food, we used the information from them to produce the lists in Apendix 3

6 The tables what the pupils sit at are to crowded, so we recommend that only six pupils sit at each table, this will be possible if we have two sessions instead of one.

Using headings

(10 marks)

A classmate prepared to write a report on her school canteen. She jotted down these points:

amount of food	crowding	behaviour of pupils	servers
tables	pupil satisfaction	quality of food	cooks
cost of food	seating	cleanliness/hygiene	taste
(un)healthy food	hours/time	queues	waste

She showed you her notes and asked you for your opinion on arranging the points.

1. Suggest **five** main headings under which most or all of the points can be put.

   _____

   _____

   _____

   _____

   _____

The pupils in Miss Wilson's class asked her if they could have a class picnic, so she asked them to plan the arrangements for a picnic. One pupil wrote about the following points but did not put them under any headings or in any clear order.

date	bus/car/train/coach	music/songs	weather – alternative indoors
times	food	drinks	parents – inform, come?
place	games	cost	activities

2. Suggest **five** main headings for a plan for the picnic.

   _____

   _____

   _____

   _____

   _____

Conditional sentences

🔑 Key idea

A conditional sentence says that one thing depends on another. Conditional sentences usually contain the words **if** or **unless**. The "if" or "unless" part of the sentence is a special type of subordinate clause called a **conditional clause**.

       conditional clause   main clause

If you tickle me, I will laugh.

What happens?

Complete these sentences in any sensible way. They are about habitual (usual) actions. *(10 marks – 2 marks for each correct sentence)*

1   If you leave ice out of a fridge, _____

2   If a player hits another player during a game of football, _____
_____

3   If people find that they have mice in their home, _____
_____

4   If it rains while the sun is shining, _____

5   If I'm very thirsty during the night, _____

What will probably happen?

Put in the right form of the verbs in brackets. The sentences are about things that may, can or probably will happen in future. *(5 marks – 0.5 mark for each correct answer)*

1   If a young child _____ (play) with matches at home, he or she _____ (start) a fire.

2   If it rains on Saturday, our Sports Day _____ (postpone). Then it _____ (hold) on 23 June.

3   If you _____ (eat) too much food, you _____ (put) on weight.

4   If you both stand on that table at the same time, it _____ (probably collapse) and you _____ (break) something.

5   If the rain doesn't stop soon, all this area _____ (flood) and we _____ (force) to leave our home.

Giving advice

We can use **If I were you ...** to give advice:

If I were you,	I wouldn't eat so much.
	I wouldn't bother to answer that email.
	I would be honest about it.

What advice can you give these friends or relatives? *(10 marks – 2 marks for each suitable answer)*

1. Dave says he always feels tired in the morning. He admits that he rarely goes to bed before 11 p.m. because his parents let him stay up to watch films.

2. You are visiting an aunt with your brother or sister. You have both been offered a cup of coffee, but you have declined the coffee politely. Your brother or sister is not sure whether or not to try drinking it and asks your advice.

3. A friend says she has several unwanted jigsaw puzzles at home. She is not sure whether to take them to a charity shop or just to throw them away. What do you advise?

4. A friend's family are going to spend a few days in Paris during the holidays. They can't decide whether to go by rail, ferry or air. Your friend mentioned this to you and said, "What would you do?"

5. A friend goes to a different school from yours. He tells you that he has noticed that two older boys are bullying younger pupils and making them pay money nearly every day. He is not sure what, if anything, he should do. He has asked for your advice. What do you suggest?

Other ways of showing a condition

We can also show a condition by making sentences like these:

You can go	provided that	you return before dark.
You can play with them	as long as	you're back by 700 p.m.
It's all right for you to go	on condition that	you are not late home again.

Use the information in each pair of sentences to make one sentence using one of the connectives in the second column above. You can change, omit or add words.
(5 marks)

1. You can go to Tom's house. You must be back here by 800 p.m.

   _____

2. You can borrow my bike. You must return it on Saturday.

   _____

3. Tom can stay with us for the weekend. His parents must agree.

   _____

4. I'll help you. Don't argue all the time.

   _____

5. We can have a picnic on Saturday. The weather must be fine then.

   _____

Narrative writing

Key idea

The purpose of a narrative text is to tell a story. Although individual stories can be very different, they all have some common structural and language features.

Zangram by C. J. Salter: extract 1

Read this extract from *Zangram*. Then answer the questions below. *(10 marks)*

> 1   The Logan family pulled wearily into a deserted car park not far from Stonehenge. Jack Logan, exhausted after driving for nine hours, said to his wife, "I need a rest."
>
>   "Good idea," his wife replied. "I told Sylvia we wouldn't be down 'til
> 5 noon."
>
>   Jack Logan glanced in the rear-view mirror. His children, Daniel and Claire, were sleeping soundly. So he settled down and was soon asleep himself.
>
>   Some time later, Claire stirred. The car seemed to be moving, but then
> 10 the movement stopped. She heard her dad snoring contentedly, and drifted back to sleep.
>
>   On board Spacecraft 462, the doors closed and a message flashed back to Zangram, far beyond Earth's solar system: "Mission completed. 20 specimens including four bipeds in a metal shell." The spaceship rose silently
> 15 from a field near Stonehenge and hurtled off into space. It carried with it the Logan family, their car, two inquisitive dogs, a deeply resentful cat and other specimens destined for examination and display in the Zangram national zoo.

1   In paragraph one, which word repeats the idea expressed by "wearily"? *(1 mark)*

_____

2   What were Mrs Logan's exact words when she spoke to Sylvia? *(1 mark)*

_____

3   What is missing before "Good idea" (line 4)? Why has it been left out? *(2 marks)*

_____

4   What adverb could we use instead of each of the following? (The adverb need not have the same meaning as the given word, but it must fit the situation.) *(4 marks)*

   a) soundly (line 7) _____   c) silently (line 14) _____

   b) contentedly (line 10) _____   d) deeply (line 16) _____

5   a) What does "inquisitive" tell us about the dogs? b) Why was the cat "resentful"? *(2 marks)*

   _____

Zangram: extract 2

Read this continuation of *Zangram*. Then answer the questions about it.
(10 marks)

1   When the Logan family woke up, they discovered they were in a huge glass dome. They were unaware, however, of the battery of tests and examinations that the Zangrams had carried out on them over a period of several days.

5   Outside the dome, a crowd of Zangrams watched the family through one-way glass. A notice outside the dome said, when translated into English, "On loan from Planet 264S/36 for 30 days". Of course, the Logans knew nothing of this. They believed that somehow they had been kidnapped.

   "Well, at least we're alive," said Mrs Logan, trying to console her
10   children. "Sooner or later, we'll find out where we are and why we're here."

   She was right. They found out the next day when the Zangrams had finally solved the riddle of Earth language and began to communicate with them.

1   What happened to the Logan family before they were put on display? *(2 marks)*

   _____

2   Why does the writer start a new paragraph in three places after the first paragraph? Give a reason why each of the three paragraphs has been started. *(3 marks)*

   _____

   _____

   _____

3   How does the phrase that begins the second paragraph link it to the first paragraph? *(2 marks)*

   _____

4   What does the pronoun "this" in line 8 refer to? *(1 mark)*

_____

5   How does the writer create a dramatic effect at the beginning of the last paragraph? *(2 marks)*

_____

Zangram: extract 3

Now read extract 3 and answer the questions about it. *(10 marks)*

> 1   When the Logans woke up in the car park at Stonehenge, they were puzzled to find their car turned round. They knew something odd had happened, but what? They drove on to Cornwall in some confusion. Their bewilderment deepened when they finally reached the home of Jack's brother and rang the
> 5   doorbell. Tony Logan opened the door and stared at them in a mixture of astonishment and horror.
>   "Where have you been?" he said at last. "We were expecting you a month ago! We checked with your neighbours. We even informed the police because …"
> 10   "A month ago!" echoed Jack Logan. "We agreed July 10th and here we are."
>   Tony stared at his brother, trying to decide whether he was joking or not. "But today is August 10th," he pointed out. "Anyway, come in. You're welcome at any time – even when you're officially 'missing, presumed dead'."
>   Mrs Logan and the children went in. Jack went back to the car to unpack
> 15   the luggage. What he saw in the boot proved that something very strange had occurred.

1   What is similar about the ways in which extracts 1, 2 and 3 end? *(2 marks)*

_____

2   "We even informed the police because …" Why does the author insert …? *(1 mark)*

_____

3   Find five *different* uses of capital letters in the extract. *(5 marks)*

_____

_____

4   Write a sentence saying what Mr Logan found in the boot. *(2 marks)*

_____

unit 17

Describing past events

Key idea

The purpose of writing a recount is to tell about a past event. Recount texts have some common structural and language features that help to identify them.

Time connectives

Read the account of a football match below. Put in ten different linking words or expressions. Choose from those below. *(10 marks)*

right up to the final whistle	shortly afterwards	at the start of the game
within the first ten minutes	ten minutes later	for the rest of the first half
during the half-time break	at half-time	ten minutes from the end
	immediately	

(1)_____ yesterday, Newtown were confidently expected to beat Oldtown by at least two goals. Newtown forced two corners (2)_____, but failed to score. Oldtown struck back but Jordan's shot was wide. (3)_____, Ken Teale put Newtown one up when he headed home a cross from Ojuro. Play was restricted to the centre of the field (4)_____ with Newtown slightly superior. (5)_____ the score remained Newtown 1 – Oldtown 0

Newtown manager, Joe Kellick, gave his men a pep-talk (6)_____. The players responded with raids on the Oldtown goal, during which Ken Teale scored his second goal. (7)_____ Oldtown veteran, Paul Cranston, scored for Oldtown. Stung by this unexpected goal, Newtown launched another series of attacks (8)_____ and were rewarded when Ojuro scored Newtown's third goal.

(9)_____ Tom Baxter shot wide for Oldtown. Defences dominated the game (10)_____.

Final score: Newtown 3 – Oldtown 1

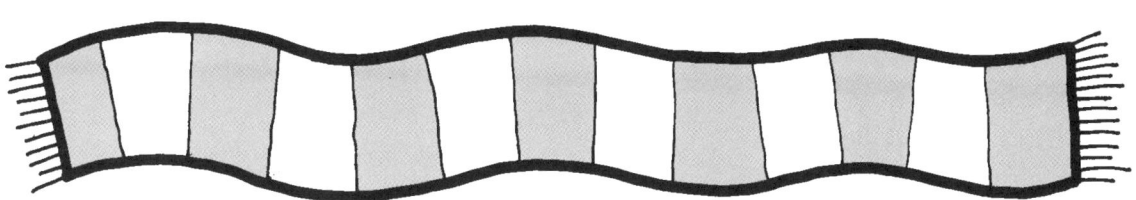

33

Exploring language

Read 'Hot water' and then answer the questions about it. *(20 marks)*

Hot water

Sue went to visit her grandfather, aged 90, in a remote rural district. Grandad cooked a very tasty lunch. However, when Sue put the plates and cutlery on the table, she noticed some tiny brown specks on her plate. She studied the plate thoughtfully for a few moments.

"Grandad," she asked hesitantly. "Are you … Are these plates clean?"

"Of course they are," Grandad replied quickly. "They're as clean as hot water can get them. That's for sure. Enjoy your meal and don't worry about the plates."

In the evening, Sue helped Grandad to prepare supper. She was hungry and was just about to put the food on the plates when she saw a thin piece of something on one of the plates. It looked like scrambled egg.

"Grandad," she said firmly. "Are you absolutely sure these plates are clean?"

"No doubt about it," Grandad said with a smile. "They're as clean as hot water can make them. I can guarantee that."

A few minutes later, a neighbour approached Grandad's house. Immediately his dog started to bark furiously. Grandad shouted angrily at the dog, "Cut that out, Hotwater! No more barking! Go and lay down! It's only Jim. You know him."

"I call her 'Hotwater'," Grandad explained to Sue, "because she always gets me into trouble."

"Ugh!" Sue thought. "I wonder if … I think I've been had."

"Grandad," she said quietly, "I'll wash the dishes tonight."

34

1   a) Underline any ten adjectives in the passage. *(5 marks)*

    b) Choose six of the adjectives and give words opposite in meaning to them. *(3 marks)*

    _____   _____

    _____   _____

    _____   _____

2   Choose three verbs used in the past tense in the passage. Write them down and then write the present and future tenses of each. *(3 marks)*

    _____

    _____

    _____

3   At the end of the third sentence, what one word can we insert after "plate" to turn the following sentence into a subordinate clause? _____ *(1 mark)*

4   Suggest a reason why Sue was hesitant when she first asked Grandad if the plates were clean? *(1 mark)*

    _____

5   Complete the sentence. *(1 mark)*

    "In line 6, the writer uses 'as … as' to_____

6   a) Write down any six adverbs in the passage. *(3 marks)*

    _____   _____

    _____   _____

    _____   _____

    b) Choose any four of the adverbs and write down words opposite in meaning to them. *(2 marks)*

7   What did Sue mean when she said, "I think I've been had"? *(1 mark)*

    _____

35

Unit 18 Giving instructions

Key idea

Instructions, directions and descriptions of procedures all have to be written clearly and concisely so they are easy to follow. Features such as sequenced and numbered steps, imperative verbs and sequencing connectives are common to this type of writing.

Checklist

Paul wrote the following checklist for maintaining his bike. Read it and then answer the questions about it. *(15 marks)*

> Checklist for maintaining bicycles
> 1. Check <u>brake</u> cables. Do brake blocks make good contact with rims of wheels?
> 2. Is <u>bell</u> fastened firmly? Does it work properly?
> 3. Check if front and rear <u>lights</u>. Replace battry or check dynamo if necessary.
> 4. <u>Chain</u> – tighten and see if any oil is needed.
> 5. <u>Saddle</u> – make sure it is at the right height and comfortable.
> 6. <u>Carrier</u> – check that nuts holding carrier are not lose. Tighten?
> 7. Check nuts holding <u>wheels</u> in place. Tighten or replace if necessary.
> 8. Check air in <u>tyres</u>; check for slow punctures.
> 9. Grease or oil any points that need lubricating, e.g. wheel <u>axils</u>.
> 10. Check that <u>tyre valves</u> are working properly.
> 11. Buy <u>padlock</u> with at least two keys. Get extra keys cut?

1. In step 2, are "firmly" and "properly" adjectives or adverbs?
   _____ *(2 marks)*

2. In step 3, what words are missing from the first sentence?
   _____ *(2 marks)*

3. How could Paul do step 5? _____ *(2 marks)*

4. Find four misspelt words and correct them. *(4 marks)*

   _____   _____

   _____   _____

5. Rewrite step 2 as a single statement with an imperative verb. *(2 marks)*

   _____

6   Which two steps could you combine so that there are only ten steps? *(2 marks)*

7   What is the purpose of step 11? *(1 mark)*

Defrosting a freezer

Rewrite Gran's instructions for how to defrost a freezer. Set them out in the right order using no more than ten steps. Leave out points that are not necessary.
(15 marks)

> Well, of course, you have to make sure that you don't make a mess in the kitchen. We don't want any water left on the floor to make the place slippery. That's how Grandad broke a leg a few years ago. Get a few old towels (there are plenty at the bottom of the airing-cupboard) and take them to the freezer. Oh, yes, you'll need a pail or a saucepan to put the water in. Put one of the towels on the floor in front of the freezer to catch the drips. Now, where was I? Ah, yes, empty the freezer. There are only a couple of packets in it now. Stick them in the fridge. Turn off the electricity. Open the freezer wide. Put a couple of towels inside to soak up the water. If you're in a hurry, put a bowl of hot water on a shelf in the freezer. It will help to thaw out the ice. You can poke any pieces of ice free if you like but it's not necessary.
>
> Leave the freezer door open and just be patient. When the ice has all gone, wring out the towels. Clean and dry the freezer. Get rid of any water. Then put the packets back in the freezer and turn it on. Easy!

Unit 19 Writing reports

🔑 Key idea

Report texts present information on a subject. They describe things as they are. They often feature present-tense verbs, descriptive adjectives and adverbs, and headings and subheadings.

The breakfast report

(10 marks)

1. "Write a report about breakfast in your family," said the teacher to Paul's class. If you were in the class, how would you arrange your ideas? Think of headings for three paragraphs. *(3 marks)*

   _____
   _____
   _____

> <u>Breakfast by Paul</u>
> We have three different kinds of breakfast, classified according to how it is eaten.
> My favourite is a "sitting-down" breakfast. It is a leisurely event on Saturday and Sunday because I do not have to get up early. It includes cereal, fried eggs, beans, mushrooms, toast and jam and a big glass of orange juice.
> A "standing-up" breakfast involves a drink, toast and a piece of fruit. I usually have this on school days because I have less time.
> When I forget to set the alarm and am late for school, I have to have an "on-the-move" breakfast. I shoot out of the house, buy a chocolate bar and eat it before the bell rings.

2. Write paragraph headings for Paul's report above. *(3 marks)*

   _____
   _____
   _____

3. What part of speech is each of these words as it is used in Paul's report? *(4 marks)*
   a) classified _____ b) leisurely _____
   c) usually _____ d) shoot _____

The rodent report

This is part of a report on squirrels, written by Sally, age 11 Read it and then answer the questions about it. *(10 marks)*

> ### Grey squirrels
> **Where they came from**
>
> Grey squirrels were brought to Britain from America many years ago and kept in zoos. Some excaped and spread to both rural and urban areas. They have now driven red squirrels away.
>
> _____
>
> They prefer to eat seeds, berries and especially nuts, so they can often be found near oak, beech and other nut trees. However, they also eat birds' eggs and baby birds. Therefore, the presents of squirrels often leads to the absence of birds since they cannot nest safely.
>
> **How they behave**
>
> Grey squirrels are active during the day and do not hibernate in winter. They are naturaly shy, but not when it comes to food. In some towns, squirrels in parks are so tame that they will take peanuts, if offered, from people's hands.
>
> **The problems they cause**
>
> Grey squirrels (in fact, all kinds of squirrels) can be pests. They raid berries and other fruit from bushes and trees in poeple's gardens. They also gnaw and eat bark, which leads to the death of trees.

1. a) Circle the passive verb in the first paragraph. *(1 mark)*
   b) Why is the verb not active? *(1 mark)* _____

2. Fill in the missing subheading for the second paragraph. *(2 marks)*

3. Draw a box around each of the connectives in the second paragraph. (Do not include "and".) *(2 marks)*

4. Find the four misspelled words in the report. Draw a line through each one and write the correctly spelled word above. *(2 marks)*

5. In the last sentence of the third paragraph, underline the main clause once and the subordinate clause twice. *(2 marks)*

Write a worm report

(10 marks)

Here are some notes about worms.
1 Think of four different headings under which you could group the notes.
2 Then write a four-paragraph report using the notes.

- Do not like light
- Eat dead leaves and soil
- Has complete digestive system
- Help plants to grow
- Live underground
- Long, soft bodies with head and tail end
- Make tunnels to move about
- No bones, eyes, legs
- Soil leaves body making worm "casts"
- Useful creatures – tunnels bring air to soil
- Use muscles and hairs on skin to move
- Take nutrients from soil as it passes through body

WORMS

Paragraph 1 heading:_____

Paragraph 2 heading:_____

Paragraph 3 heading:_____

Paragraph 4 heading:_____

Unit 20: Persuasive writing

Key idea

Persuasive writing aims to influence the reader towards a particular opinion. It often uses emotional words, figurative devices and imperative verbs.

Email scam

Mrs Stone received this email, which is full of mistakes. Fortunately, she knew it was not from her bank at all, but an attempt by someone to find out her details illegally. Read it and answer the questions. *(10 marks)*

> Subject: Confirm your details to avoid immediate cancellation to your account.
>
> Yesterday the bank have a failure of its software this resulted in a lost of customer data. To help you to avoid from fraud, kindly connect with the link below to confirm your account registration data, this is obligatory to protect your account.
>
> Please do not answer to this message. Fill in the form "Confirmation of Acount Details".

1. Which words in the "subject" are meant to frighten the receiver? *(1 mark)*

2. Find an incorrect verb tense. Explain why it is wrong and correct it. *(2 marks)*

3. Find two places where punctuation is wrong or missing. Correct them. *(2 marks)*

4. Find and correct four expressions in which prepositions are used wrongly. *(2 marks)*

5. Find and correct two spelling mistakes. *(2 marks)*

6. Why does the sender of the email put in the sentence, "This is obligatory to protect your account"? *(1 mark)*

The mighty T-watch is here: hep, handy, helpful!

It's COOL and it could be yours!

On one side, it's a watch.
No need to look at it.

Press the button and it tells you the time. Now that's really something – but there's more!

On the other side? A nifty recorder. Up to 10 minutes talktime. No need to take notes.

**Move up to the in-crowd!
ORDER NOW
before they're all snapped up.**

"I love it!" says pop star Kati Lane.

Football legend, Mike O'Shea:
"I wouldn't be without mine!"

An advertisement

Read the advertisement above and then answer these questions. *(10 marks)*

1 Which slang words in the advertisment mean "up-to-date, fashionable"? *(1 mark)*

2 What figurative device is used in the second line? *(1 mark)*

3 Why is "COOL" put in capital letters? *(1 mark)*

4 "On the other side? A nifty recorder." Explain why the writer doesn't use complete sentences. *(2 marks)*

5 Why does the advertiser use the word "nifty" instead of "clever"? *(1 mark)*

6 Explain the purpose of the pictures. *(2 marks)*

7 Give one example each of two different verb forms used in the advertisement. *(1 mark)*

8 In the first draft of this advertisement, the advertiser wrote : "Keep up with the in-crowd". Why did she change this to "Move up to the in-crowd"? *(1 mark)*

Getting involved

Miss Benson's class wrote to their local council following three traffic accidents near their school. Read their first draft below and then answer the questions.

(10 marks)

> In the passed six months, there have been three horrific traffic acidents near our school, each time somebody was knocked down by a speeding motorist. We beg the Council to do something to make Bridge Street safer.
>
> We would like to recommend four crucial measures. First of all, we hope the Council can put some speed bumps in the road to slow down traffic. Secondly, we need a pedestran crossing outside our school. Thirdly, it would be a good idea to errect warning sines at each end of Bridge Street, finally, we think that cars should not be aloud to park outside our school for longer than 15 minutes during 8–9 a.m. and 3–4 p.m. on school days.

1. Why do the children mention accidents in their letter? *(1 mark)*

2. Give two examples of powerful, emotive words in the letter. Why do the children use them? *(2 marks)*

3. Find and correct six spelling mistakes in the draft letter. *(3 marks)*

4. Find two places where a comma should be replaced by a full stop. *(1 mark)*

5. Find a passive verb in the first paragraph. *(1 mark)*

6. List the sequencing connectives used in the second paragraph. *(1 mark)*

7. How might the children revise the layout of the second paragraph so that their suggestions are clearer? *(1 mark)*

Unit 21 Writing discussion texts

🔑 Key idea

Discussion texts give a balanced presentation of all the various positions that are held about an issue or topic – for example, both sides of an argument.

Television: points of view

"Does television do more harm than good?" Read the first draft of what one pupil wrote and then answer the questions about it. *(10 marks)*

1 Most television shows have a bad influence to viewers, especially young ones. They use swear words and bad language most of the time. Violence is common in "soaps" and are regarded as a model or example to teenagers.
   On the other hand, documentries are both educational and intresting. There is always
5 something new for viewers to learn as long as they can stay awake. Oddly enough, the cartoons are usually OK. They are always amusing without setting a bad example. Sports programmes are also worth watching and do not cause no harm or offence.
   Maybe the only fair answer to the question is that the affect of TV depends upon the individual. If you have firm principals, you can always chose wisely. I hope that television
10 channels will clean up their act, but I won't hold my breathe waiting for that to happen.

1 What more accurate word should the writer use instead of "most" in lines 1 and 2? *(1 mark)*

2 In lines 1 and 3, replace "to" with correct prepositions. *(2 marks)*

3 Explain and correct the error of agreement in the third sentence. *(1 mark)*

4 Explain and correct the error in the last sentence of the second paragraph. *(1 mark)*

5 Correct six spelling mistakes in the last two paragraphs. *(3 marks)*

6 Is the writer's discussion well-balanced? Explain your answer. *(2 marks)*

Maths – or no maths?

"Should children be allowed to decide whether they want to study maths or not?" Read the first draft of what one pupil wrote and then answer the questions about it. *(10 marks)*

1 Some people say that we do not need maths in our daily lifes because calculaters and computers can give us all the answers. I don't agree to that because sometimes if we don't know any maths it is easy for crooks to cheat us. Also we need maths whenever we buy or sell anything and maybe we have no calculator available.

5 On the other hand, it is true that algebra and geometry can be too difficult to some children and they become confused and fed up. Then they may even hate the subject and start to behave badly at school. Perhaps the right thing to do is to make basic maths compulsery up to, say, the age of 14 and to make it optional after that. If somebody is no good at maths (even when he or she tries very hard), it is a waist of time to force the

10 person to continue to study the subject.

1 Find and correct four spelling errors: two in each paragraph *(2 marks)*

2 Correct the mistakes in the use of prepositions in lines 2 and 5 *(1 mark)*

3 What more formal words could the writer use instead of "crooks" (line 3) and "fed up" (line 6)? *(1 mark)*

4 How many points for each side of the argument does the writer give? What are they? *(4 marks)*

5 Do you agree with the writer's conclusion? Give reasons for your answer. *(2 marks)*

Should it be a crime to kill any wild animal?

(10 marks)

Put a suitable word in each blank space. *(7 marks – 0.5 mark for each correct answer)*

I am in favour of protecting wild animals, but there (1)_____ two main reasons (2)_____ I do not think it (3)_____ be a crime to kill any wild animal. Firstly, sometimes it is (4)_____ to kill wild animals such as mice, rats and rabbits. (5)_____ we do not kill some of them, they will increase (6)_____ cause serious problems. A (7)_____ reason is that sometimes wild animals, such (8)_____ boars, foxes, badgers and deer, increase and (9)_____ a threat to farmers. Then it is necessary to kill some of (10)_____.

We must also remember (11)_____ some farmers keep cattle, sheep, deer, goats and (12)_____ animals for their milk or meat. Are these wild animals? If somebody kills a wild pony on Dartmoor (13)_____ that a crime? As I said earlier, I think some wild animals should be protected, but making it a crime to kill one is not the (14)_____ way of doing it.

- **Do you think it should be a crime to kill wild animals? Give two reasons for your answer.** *(3 marks)*

_____
_____
_____
_____
_____

Unit 22

Investigating English expressions

 **Key idea** ....

Investigating language is the best way to find out how it works.

American English ....

(16 marks)

Americans speak English, but many of their words differ from British English. Do you know what they're talking about? Put the right British word by each American word below. *(8 marks – 0.5 mark for each correct answer)*

| taxi   pavement   sweets   dummy (for a baby)   nappy   trousers |
| autumn   boot (of a car)   lorry   curtains   petrol   sweet biscuits |
| lift   handbag   queue   tap (for water) |

1 cab _____

2 line _____

3 fall _____

4 truck _____

5 diaper _____

6 purse _____

7 candy _____

8 pants _____

9 trunk (of a car) _____

10 gas(oline) _____

11 pacifier _____

12 cookies _____

13 faucet _____

14 sidewalk _____

15 drapes _____

16 elevator _____

Now find out for yourself the British words for these American words. *(8 marks)*

17 drugstore _____

18 closet _____

19 stove _____

20 hood (of a car) _____

21 vacation _____

22 garbage _____

23 movies _____

24 buck (money) _____

47

Investigating idioms

Put the right idiom on each line below. *(14 marks)*

- a Tartar
- eyewash
- a close shave
- a mouthpiece
- a square peg in a round hole
- a rough diamond
- a pig in a poke
- a fool's paradise
- a blank cheque
- a fly in the ointment
- a red herring
- a hornets' nest
- soft soap
- a white lie

1 A _____ is an untrue statement which is made for good reasons, for example to protect an innocent person.

2 _____ is something (usually a statement) meant to deceive people or hide something wrong.

3 _____ is a person who is very difficult to deal with even if you have some advantage over them. Many years ago, if you captured this person in a battle, he would prove a troublesome prisoner.

4 _____ is something which is meant to deceive you, perhaps by making you look in the wrong direction when trying to solve a problem.

5 _____ is permission to do as you like, for example to spend as much money as you like because the cheque has been signed but no amount has been put in.

6 If you spend a lot of time dreaming about winning a lottery, you may live in _____, thinking about something nice which will never happen.

7 If you buy _____, you buy something (such as a pig tied up in a sack) before you have had a chance to inspect it.

8 _____ is flattery.

9 _____ is somebody who appears tough or lacking in manners, but is really very kind and generous.

10 If a person is in a job that does not suit him or her, we may say that the person is _____.

11 _____ is an obstacle to a plan.

12 Sometimes we call a narrow escape _____.

13 _____ is somebody who speaks on behalf of another person or organisation, often to give excuses or reasons for an action.

14 _____ is a source of possible trouble because if you interfere you may create a worse situation.

Key Grammar is a brand new resource, specifically planned to cover all the key grammar objectives in self-contained units of work. The pupil books feature:

- clear, progressive units covering all key learning objectives
- plenty of practice and consolidation work
- opportunities to challenge and extend children's learning
- a clear mark scheme
- exercises in an appropriate context, with engaging illustrations

The workbooks provide activities for additional practice, differentiation, and homework. The important language skills coverage in **Key Grammar** is complemented by two associated series: **Key Comprehension** and **Key Spelling** – up-to-date and engaging resources which reinforce key teaching points and enable children to practise, consolidate and extend their learning. For further information about **Key Comprehension** and **Key Spelling** call our Customer Services Department on **(+44) (0)1865 888000**.

ISBN 978-0-602206-85-7

Author: Alan Etherton

Ginn is an imprint of Pearson education Limited, a company incorporated in England and Wales, having its registered office at Edinburgh Gate, Harlow, Essex, CM20 2JE.
Registered company number: 872828

www.ginn.co.uk
Help and support for teachers plus the widest range of education solutions

© Harcourt Education Limited 2005

This book is copyright and reproduction of the whole or part without the publishers' written permission is prohibited.

Key Grammar Workbook 4
ISBN: 978 0602 20685 7
Level 4 Easy Order Pack: 978 0602 20651 2
Level 4 Workbook 6 Pack: 978 0602 20648 2

First published 2005

16
13

Cover illustration by Pet Gotohda
Cover design by Tom Cole
Designed by Nicki Wise, Te Marama Design
Illustrations by David Semple, Gary Swift, Andrew Painter

Printed and bound in China (GCC/13)

 # Grammar Workbook 4

Contents

Unit 1	Word classes	page 2
Unit 2	Using standard English	page 4
Unit 3	Active and passive verbs 1	page 6
Unit 4	Connectives	page 8
Unit 5	Forming complex sentences 1	page 10
Unit 6	Punctuation	page 12
Unit 8	Active and passive verbs 2	page 14
Unit 9	Official language	page 16
Unit 10	Forming complex sentences 2	page 18
Unit 11	Making notes	page 20
Unit 12	Writing a summary	page 22
Unit 13	Editing	page 24
Unit 14	Conditional sentences	page 27
Unit 16	Narrative writing	page 30
Unit 17	Describing past events	page 33
Unit 18	Giving instructions	page 36
Unit 19	Writing reports	page 38
Unit 20	Persuasive writing	page 41
Unit 21	Writing discussion texts	page 44
Unit 22	Investigating English expressions	page 47

Unit 1: Word classes

🔑 Key idea

Words are categorised in classes according to the jobs they do in a sentence: noun, pronoun, verb, adjective, adverb, preposition, conjunction and interjection. Words can belong to more than one class.

Work it out

Give one-word answers. *(10 marks)*

1. Which proper noun is the name of the Italian capital? _____
2. Which adjective is the opposite of "wise"? _____
3. Which collective noun means "a lot of (birds flying) together"? _____
4. Which verb means "to tremble with cold or fear"? _____
5. Which pronoun is the opposite of "no one"? _____
6. Which proper noun is the name of the shortest month of the year? _____
7. Which adverb is the opposite of "rarely"? _____
8. What is the second part of the conjunction "not only…"? _____
9. What adverb can we form from "skill"? _____
10. Which verb means to "make longer"? _____

Which word?

Ring or underline the right word in the brackets. *(10 marks)*

1. It was dark, so we couldn't see (nothing, anything) clearly.
2. Would you mind (to wait, waiting) a few minutes?
3. There (are, is) more than one way of solving this problem.
4. Where (are, is) the rest of the players?
5. The change in the plan will not have a great deal of (affect, effect) on us.
6. Don't be so (impatience, impatient), John!
7. Between you and (I, me), I think Margaret is quite right to be suspicious.
8. This photo is different (than, from) that one.
9. We watched the marathon, but we did not (took, take) part in it.
10. Your new bike is much better than (Paul's, Pauls').

Classify it

Read this passage from *Nicholas Nickleby* by Charles Dickens. Place each of the underlined words under the correct heading in the grid below. *(10 marks – 0.5 mark for each correctly placed word)*

Dotheboy's Hall <u>was</u> not a hall at all, <u>but</u> a bare and dirty room with a <u>couple</u> of windows, in which most of the glass was broken. There were a few old <u>rickety</u> desks, <u>cut</u> and notched, and inked and damaged, in <u>every</u> possible way; a detached desk for <u>Squeers</u>; and another <u>for</u> his assistant. The ceiling was supported, like <u>that</u> of a barn, by cross beams and rafters; and the walls were so stained that it was impossible to tell <u>whether</u> they had ever been painted or whitewashed.

But the pupils! How his last hopes <u>faded</u> as <u>he</u> looked <u>around</u>! Pale and haggard faces of old men, boys of stunted growth, and others whose long thin legs would <u>hardly</u> carry their <u>stooping</u> bodies, all <u>crowded</u> together; there were the bleary eye, the hare-lip, the crooked foot, and every problem arising from <u>cruelty</u> and neglect. There were little faces which should have been handsome, darkened with the scowl of suffering; there were vicious-faced boys, brooding like prisoners in jail; <u>and</u> there were children <u>who</u> were weeping <u>with</u> loneliness…

nouns	
pronouns	
verbs	
adjectives	
adverbs	
prepositions	
conjunctions	

Unit 2 Using standard English

Key idea

We can use non-standard English in speech, but we must use standard English in formal written work.

Does it agree?

Underline the subject each time. (It may be a single word or a group of words.) Then circle the right word in the brackets so that the verb agrees with its subject.
(14 marks)

1. How much of the information in newspaper reports or radio and television news reports (are, is) completely accurate?

2. According to a report on television, a reward of several thousand pounds (has, have) been offered for information leading to the arrest of the robbers.

3. The driver of the bus – together with two of the passengers – (was, were) slightly injured in the accident.

4. (Is, Are) there any mud on your shoes?

5. The number of flights from London to Spain (have, has) risen in recent years because more people like to spend a holiday on the Spanish coast.

6. There (is, are) a number of reasons why people prefer to spend their holiday abroad. The main attraction is the better climate overseas.

7. What a nuisance! All the traffic (has, have) stopped. There must have been an accident somewhere ahead of us.

8. Before the play started, a member of the cast peeped through the curtains and said, "Oh, good! The audience (is, are) a really big one tonight. There are no empty seats."

9. Everybody in our class (want, wants) to join in the picnic, don't they?

10. How long (has, have) all this rubbish been lying here?

11. As a result of a change in the law, the poor (is, are) likely to be better off.

12. A good standard of numeracy (is, are) necessary in many jobs.

13. At least a third of those players (is, are) from foreign countries.

14. The majority of the pupils in our class (does, do) not come to school in a car.

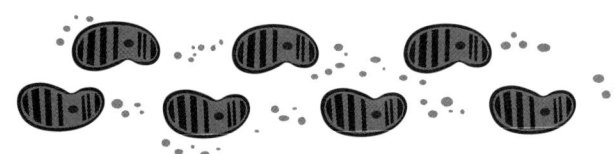

Choose the right word

Ring or underline the right words in the brackets. *(8 marks)*

1 This shop doesn't sell cosmetics (or, nor) health foods.

2 My sister doesn't like garlic and (so, nor) do I.

3 Sometimes people are not sure where to keep their money. If they hide (them, it) at home, there is always a risk of burglary.

4 The manager told his staff that he hadn't (no, any) intention of resigning.

5 John did not feel very well at the start of the cross-country race, and he felt much (worse, worser) at the end.

6 After the show, my friend and (me, I) bought some chips and ate (it, them) on the way home.

7 We need somebody to check all the electrical (equipment, equipments) before we turn on the computer and heating.

8 Our visit to Scandinavia (maybe, may be) described as a tour rather than a holiday.

Make it formal

Write more formal expressions that we can use instead of the italic words. *(8 marks)*

1 That's a *lousy* idea. _____

2 There's a rumour that their business is *on the rocks*. _____

3 All the *kids* in my class agree with me. _____

4 I haven't got *nothing* special to tell you. _____

5 The man said he didn't know *no one* with that name. _____

6 The fact that he is guilty *sticks out like a sore thumb*. _____

7 This hairstyle is gradually *catching on*. _____

8 *How come* you're not at school today? _____

Active and passive verbs 1

🔑 Key idea

Verbs can be in the **active** or **passive** voice.

A dangerous job

Write in the *passive* Simple Present form of the verbs in brackets. *(12 marks)*

In Malaysia, rubber (1)_____ (grow) on many estates. At dawn, rubber-tappers start work. Many of them are women and they know that their work can be dangerous. Sometimes tappers (2)_____ (attack) by a tiger. When they bend down to tap a tree, they (3)_____ (sometimes mistake) for a wild animal and attacked by a hungry tiger.

Tappers start work before the sun rises. First, a cut (4)_____ (make) in a mature tree. A tin or half a coconut shell (5)_____ (fasten) to the tree. It (6)_____ (use) to collect latex from the cut. The tapper cuts many trees. Then he or she returns to the first tree. Latex in the tin (7)_____ (empty) into a pail which (8)_____ (take) to the small "factory" on the estate. Chemicals (9)_____ (add) to the latex and mixed in well. Later on, the latex (10)_____ (squeeze) into sheets which (11)_____ (hang) in a smoke-filled hut. Finally, the sheets of rubber (12)_____ (tie) up in bales, ready for export to other countries.

A gas leak

Put in the *passive* form of the verbs in brackets. Use *has/have been + a past participle* each time. *(10 marks)*

One evening Mrs Wilson (Mrs W) was on her way home from work. She got off a bus and started to walk the 200 metres to her home. As she walked round a corner, she was surprised to see a crowd of people outside a wrecked house. There were fire-engines and police cars there too. Mrs Wilson's friend, Mrs Johnson (Mrs J), was in the crowd.

Mrs W: What's the matter? What's happened?

Mrs J: There was a gas leak. That house (1)_____ (wreck) completely.

Mrs W: (2)_____ anybody _____ (injure)?

Mrs J: Yes, two people (3)_____(hurt). They (4)_____ (take) to hospital already.

Mrs W: What are the fire-engines doing here?

Mrs J: There was a small fire but it (5)_____ (bring) under control. The gas company (6)_____ (inform), so men are coming to repair the pipe. A lot of debris (7)_____ (hurl) across the road, so the windows in those houses (8)_____ (break). The people in those houses (9)_____ (evacuate). There were some elderly people in that old folks' home over there. They (10) _____ (move) to another home temporarily.

Mrs W: Is there anything we can do to help?

Mrs J: No, I don't think so.

In trouble

Put in the *passive* future form of the verbs in brackets. Use *will be + a past participle*. *(8 marks)*

Paul's friend, Mike, was sent off during a football match for hitting an opponent. Now Paul is asking his dad, a referee, what will happen to Mike.

Paul: Will Mike get into trouble?

Dad: Yes, I'm afraid he will. I'm sure he (1)_____ (charge) with hitting an opponent. Then he (2)_____ (ask) to attend a hearing before the Disciplinary Committee. He (3)_____ (tell) what he is charged with.

Paul: What will happen after that?

Dad: He (4)_____ (give) a chance to listen to the referee's report and ask any questions. Then he (5)_____ (invite) to make his statement and admit the charge or try to deny it.

Paul: I don't think he will deny it because everybody saw what happened. What will the Committee do?

Dad: Well, Mike (6)_____ (inform) of the decision in writing. It is probable that he (7)_____ (ban) for a few months. If he has a bad record, he (8)_____ (fine) as well, I should think.

Unit 4 Connectives

Key idea

Connectives are words and phrases that are used to link different parts of a text. They can join words, phrases, clauses, sentences and paragraphs.

Types of connectives

Underline the connectives in the sentences below. Then put them under the correct heading in the grid. *(10 marks)*

1. Paul decided to buy the bicycle although it was expensive.
2. We can go out when the rain stops.
3. Mary stuck a stamp on the envelope and then she posted the invitation.
4. Following my operation, I developed an infection in the wound.
5. We can go for a picnic on Saturday if the weather is good.
6. Mike can't go out to play now because he hasn't finished his homework yet.
7. You can go to London by train or you can travel on the express bus.
8. Our new house is bigger than our old one. Moreover, it has a large garden.
9. Most people like Susan, but I think she is rather conceited.
10. Despite having a terrible cold, the soprano performed her solo.

Addition	Time	Cause and effect	Opposition

Connective starters

Complete each sentence in a suitable way to show that you understand the connective. *(10 marks)*

1 We'll have to wait here until _____

2 If you eat too much, _____

3 We couldn't move the wardrobe because _____

4 Although it snowed last night, _____

5 In spite of the cold weather, _____

6 Kate is very fond of animals, so _____

7 Choose your sweets and then _____

8 I forgot to set the alarm. As a result, _____

9 The game started on time despite _____

10 I often eat fish. However, _____

Choosing connectives

Ring or underline the right word in the brackets. *(10 marks)*

1 We can go there by taxi. (Alternately, Alternatively) we can take the bus.

2 (Despite, In spite) the discount, Mrs Lee decided not to buy the car.

3 We had to leave our house when a pipe burst. Now we're waiting for the workmen to complete the repairs. In the (while, meantime), we're staying with my grandparents.

4 The team has succeeded because the owner of the club is a billionaire. (Nevertheless, Furthermore) it has one of the best managers in Europe.

5 Crocodiles have no predators to attack them. (Consequently, Subsequently) they manage to live for many years.

6 Trees can spread their seeds in many ways. (Meanwhile, For example,) sycamore seeds have "wings" to help them fly away from the parent tree.

7 We don't agree with Paul's plan. On the (other hand, contrary), we think it could be disastrous for the club.

8 His plan contains several faults. (Nevertheless, Similarly) it contains some good points.

9 You ought to buy yourself a watch (instead of, in spite of) borrowing mine.

10 Most shops have security cameras (providing, so that) they can catch thieves.

Unit 5: Forming complex sentences 1

Key idea

Complex sentences are made up of more than one clause. The clauses can be joined in different ways.

Completing sentences

Complete these sentences in any sensible way. Draw a ring round the connecting words. *(10 marks)*

1 A library is a place where _____

2 There was a hidden cottage where_____

3 Don't forget to turn the lights off when _____

4 People go to a dentist when _____

5 Plants will usually grow well if _____

6 Traffic police may stop a motorist if _____

7 Mary had the flu last week, so _____

8 Paul could not hear what people were saying on television, so _____
_____

9 You can go to your friend's house now, provided that _____
_____

10 You can borrow my bike if you like, provided that _____
_____

What and where?

Complete each sentence by saying *what* people are doing and *where* they are doing it. Start with a present participle (an –ing word) *(10 marks)*

Example: We watched some men **repairing** a pipe in the road near our home.

1 Ashra heard two women _____

2 When I came out of my house, I noticed a man _____
_____

3 When we reached the beach, we saw some fishermen _____
_____

4 Before we entered the park, we stopped to watch some boys _____
_____

5 When Sue looked out of the window, she saw a blackbird _____
_____

6 Last night on television we watched some girls _____
_____

7 After a few minutes, the fox came to a field and was happy to see some lambs
_____

8 Mr Evans woke up during the night when he heard somebody _____
_____

9 When our bus passed Mary's house, we saw her father _____
_____

10 The lifeguard ran down the beach when he heard somebody_____
_____

Punctuating complex sentences

Put in the missing commas. *(10 marks)*

1 Yesterday in broad daylight the police caught two men trying to rob a bank.

2 The frightened rabbit stayed absolutely still hoping that the fox had not seen it.

3 My father the manager of the store starts work before 8 a.m.

4 Last night the temperature in most Welsh towns was above freezing-point. In Aberystwyth however it was minus four degrees.

5 Did you enjoy yourself at the party last Saturday Kate?

6 Although the concert lasted for over two hours the audience was captivated by the soloist who was only ten.

7 Not having seen her cousin for several years Sue was surprised to see how tall he was.

8 Birmingham is a very large city. In fact it is one of the largest in the United Kingdom.

9 When the phone rang Peter hurried to answer it hoping that it was his friend.

10 Leaping over the wall the frightened animal disappeared into the woods.

Punctuation

🔑 Key idea

Adding clauses increases the complexity of sentences, so more punctuation is required.

Using commas

Put in commas where necessary. The sentences show various different uses of commas. *(10 marks)*

1 The home of the Duke of Devonshire has 173 rooms and houses more than 60 types of clocks.

2 Paul go and find Mary please.

3 Worms are probably the most common bait for fish. If you expect to catch fish therefore you must be prepared to handle worms.

4 'Ugh! I'm not going to touch a worm' Katie said.

5 One of our neighbours Mrs Collins is a very experienced nurse.

6 Even if I were a billionaire I would not want to live alone in a huge isolated house.

7 Very few people read poetry books in their leisure time. Many modern pop songs however contain their own type of poetry and are very popular.

8 When tadpoles get older their tails get shorter their legs get longer and they gradually develop into very small frogs.

9 Pauline Taylor whose father is a maths teacher is always top of the class in maths not surprisingly.

10 If you're ready it's time for us to leave for the airport Grandad.

Using speech marks

Each of these unpunctuated sentences contains direct speech. Rewrite them, putting in the speech marks and other punctuation marks and capital letters that are necessary. *(10 marks)*

1 My friend said to me would you mind checking this letter for me please

2 I told her you've left an r out of preferred

3 Miss Lee told me you should have written chose and not choose

4 I heard Paul shout out wait for me Mike so we waited for him

5 If you've finished your homework my mother said you can watch the film on TV

6 when the performance ended the audience rose to their feet and shouted bravo

7 clamouring up the treacherous rocks the mountain rescuer cried hold on

8 can i follow you asked grace i dont know the way besides its dark

9 the wizard whose wand was misbehaving shook his finger and said abracadabra

10 louise rubbed her eyes yawned and mumbled whats the matter

More punctuation practice

Put in any necessary punctuation marks and capital letters. *(10 marks)*

1 its the end of march tomorrow remember to put your clocks on an hour

2 remember what people say in america spring forward fall back

3 in sentence 2 the word fall means autumn

4 there are 24 children in our class 14 boys and 10 girls

5 i think that jacket is a real bargain don't you mary

6 that was my first visit to a zoo I thought it was very interesting

7 come in sit down would you like a soft drink

8 some girls like to play netball or rounders others prefer hockey

9 the speaker promised the people many things more jobs higher pay longer holidays and lower taxes

10 don't forget the saying nothing ventured nothing gained

Unit 8: Active and passive verbs 2

Key idea

Verbs can be in the **active** or **passive** voice.

Look to the future

Read the two passages. Write in the *passive* future form of the verbs in brackets.
(10 marks)

A. Tomorrow part of the motorway (1)_____ (close) for urgent resurfacing. The work (2)_____ (complete) by 4 p.m., when the road (3)_____ (reopen) to traffic. While the road is closed, traffic (4)_____ (divert). Notices (5)_____ (put) up to show motorists the route to follow.

B. Miss Harris told her class, "Our Sports Day will be on next Friday. It (6)_____ (hold) on the school field, starting at noon. All lessons will be (7)_____ (cancel) for the afternoon of that day. All parents (8)_____ (invite) to come. If bad weather is forecast, you (9)_____ (tell) and Sports Day (10)_____ (postpone) to the following week."

Will, may or must?

Read these sentences carefully. Then decide whether to put in *will*, *may* or *must*.
(10 marks)

1 This letter is urgent. It _____ be posted as soon as possible.

2 During a thunderstorm, don't shelter under a tree. It _____ be hit by lightning. If it is hit, you _____ be killed or seriously injured.

3 Be careful if you see an adder. It is a venomous snake with black zigzag marks on its top. Don't go near or touch an adder. If you do, you _____ be bitten. Then you _____ be taken to hospital. You _____ be given an antidote to fight the venom from the snake.

4 Check your bike before you go for a long ride. The brakes _____ be checked and the tyres _____ be pumped up if necessary.

5 When people return from a holiday overseas, their passports _____ be checked by an Immigration Officer. Then their luggage _____ be searched by a Customs Officer.

Active to passive

Change these sentences so that they contain *passive* verbs instead of active ones. Leave out the italic words. *(10 marks)*

1 *Somebody* stole Mr Jackson's car during the night.
   _____

2 Before the dentist drilled my tooth, *she* gave me an injection.
   _____

3 *Some workmen* pulled down that old factory last week.
   _____

4 *The strong wind* blew down two trees last night.
   _____

5 *Somebody* has just taken Mrs Sharpe to hospital.
   _____

6 *Two dustmen* collect our rubbish every Friday.
   _____

7 *People* grow a lot of apples in this part of the country.
   _____

8 *Sharks or other large fish* sometimes attack swimmers not far from the beach.
   _____

9 *The Mayor* will open the new school tomorrow.
   _____

10 *Several workmen* will redecorate our school during the holidays.
    _____

Unit 9 Official language

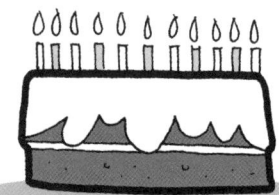

Key idea

Formal and official documents have certain language features that distinguish them from informal writing.

Informal: first person (personal); colloquial/slang vocabulary; use of contractions; short, simple sentences; exclamations, questions

Formal: third person (impersonal); technical, subject-specific vocabulary; no contractions; complex sentences; statements

---

Len Benton sent his friend, Mary Evans, a fake formal letter from a firm of solicitors when she wanted to borrow his bicycle. Mary decided to continue the game with Len. She sent him this invitation to her birthday party.

> On behalf of Miss Mary Evans, we have very considerable pleasure in requesting the pleasure of your company at a sumptuous festive social gathering of young attractive females and boisterous males to celebrate the eleventh anniversary of her blessed nativity.
>
> Please be informed accordingly that this joyful event will take place at Miss Evans' ancestral place of residence at 462 Rowan Road on Saturday 25 April, commencing punctually at 4 p.m. and drawing to a close by 8 p.m.
>
> To enable us to make adequate preparations, we would greatly appreciate it if you would kindly get in touch with us and indicate whether or not you will be able to join all concerned in this celebration. Kindly let us know what you decide before noon on 21 April so that our plans may be finalised well in advance. Alternatively, you may prefer to make your decision known directly to Mary (by phone, email, fax or in person).
>
> We are asked to pass on to all guests Mary's particular request that presents should not be brought or sent.

What do they mean?

Find and underline the expressions in Mary's invitation that have these meanings.
(10 marks)

1 are happy
2 to invite
3 party
4 children
5 birthday
6 note (verb)
7 home
8 finishing
9 would like
10 everybody

In translation

Len's brother asked him what was in the letter from Mary. Pretend you are Len. Tell your brother – in everyday English – what the main points of the invitation are. *(10 marks)*

_____
_____
_____
_____
_____
_____

Keep it simple

Give the meaning of the expressions in italics. Use ordinary, everyday English that makes the meaning clear but uses fewer words. *(10 marks)*

1 Please *contact him in writing*. _____

2 Write your name here, *giving your surname and all given names*.
   _____

3 *In the event that* you are unable to come, bring a note when you recover.
   _____

4 Mike missed a lot of lessons at school *as a result* of illness.
   _____

5 Ask a parent or *the person who is legally responsible for looking after you* to write a note to your teacher, explaining why you were absent.
   _____

6 Peter cannot come today because he is *suffering from some illness*.
   _____

7 The *man who has been accused of robbery but has not yet been tried or convicted* will give evidence tomorrow.
   _____

8 Mr Macdonald is a farmer, so he would like to *wipe out and completely get rid of* all the rabbits on his farm.
   _____

9 Your claim for compensation will be *studied in detail to ascertain all aspects of the problem*.
   _____

10 You will be told *what is eventually decided by officials who look into your case*.
   _____

Unit 10: Forming complex sentences 2

Key idea

subordinate clause   main clause   subordinate clause

After the party, we all went straight home because it was late.

There are different types of subordinate clauses. They are linked to the main clause with connectives.

Adding connectives

Put one of the following connectives in each blank space below. *(10 marks)*

if	after	before	although	when	so
while	despite	provided	so	that	

1   I have a poster that reminds me to wash my hands _____ I have a meal, and to clean my teeth _____ I have eaten anything.

2   _____ Mum agrees, we're going to have a barbecue this evening _____ it doesn't rain.

3   The house in Elm Street was too expensive and _____ my parents decided not to buy it _____ we all liked it very much

4   You can borrow these videos but let me have them back _____ Mary can watch them _____ she returns from holiday.

5   The fire started _____ men were carrying out repairs. It destroyed the whole building _____ the efforts of the firemen.

Punctuating complex sentences

Punctuate these sentences correctly. Don't forget to put in capital letters where necessary. *(10 marks – 2 marks for each correct sentence)*

1 we expected toms friend to come at 5 pm however he didnt arrive until 530
   _____

2 in the middle of lunch a boy rushed into the canteen shouting fire fire
   _____

3 I put my books away and turned off the light then I went to bed
   _____

4 when the phone rang maya picked it up expecting to hear her friends voice
   _____

5 the answer peter gave although partially correct was not the right one
   _____

Joining sentences

Join each group of sentences to make one sentence. You can change, add or omit words. *(10 marks – 2.5 marks for each correct sentence)*

1 The rain stopped. We played in the garden. The grass was still wet. We were quite chilly.
   _____
   _____

2 The girl won lots of money. She gave half of it to charity. She is Janet's cousin.
   _____
   _____

3 This is the ring. My aunt gave it to me. I was ten then. It is beautiful.
   _____
   _____

4 Uncle George is over fifty. He completed the marathon. He raised lots of money for charity.
   _____
   _____

Making notes

Key idea

We make notes to extract the most important points from written words (such as information text) or spoken words (such as a telephone conversation or interview). We write them down in a shorter form.

Babysitting

You are babysitting for Mrs Done. You receive some phone calls and need to jot down notes so that you can write out messages for her. Make notes. *(10 marks)*

1. Is that Connie Jackson? Oh, well, maybe I could leave a message for her. My name is Peter Brown. I was going to call on her tomorrow at her office at about ten but something has come up, so I can't make it. Please ask her to phone my secretary at 099-438 tomorrow to fix another appointment. Thursday or Friday would be fine for me, ideally in the morning. Thanks. Goodbye.

2. Can I interest you in a good deal on double-glazing? This week we're offering … Oh, I see. Hmmm. Well, perhaps you'd tell her that Glunk Glass have this special offer next week, for seven days only. We're offering a discount of twenty-five per cent for two windows or more. If further details are needed, ask the lady to phone Andrew Brown at 047-738 any time. Thanks.

Customer services

You are learning the work in the Customer Services Department of a busy store. People phone, so you have to take notes and then tell the manager what the complaint is about. Read what these people said to you. Make notes. *(10 marks)*

1. My name's Ivy Trott. What's that? No, I'm not related to her. What I want to do is complain about the Milky Way Mousse. Don't get me wrong. I like them very much, but you never seem to have any in stock. What's happened? Are the staff eating them all? How come you've never got any on sale? Please ask somebody to order some more, pronto!

2 I want to complain about the tomatoes in your fruit and vegetable section. I usually buy a packet of six. Twice I've found that two of the tomatoes were bad underneath. They look all right on top but when you get them out – that's a different story. Maybe you could have a word with your order clerk or whoever does the ordering and change your supplier. I'll check up on them in the coming weeks and let you know if I see any improvement. I will be bringing back the two bad ones I bought this week and will expect a refund.

Local newspaper reporter

You are a reporter in the office of a local newspaper. You receive these phone calls. Make notes of the important points. *(10 marks)*

1 In the past week, six cars have been damaged by hooligans in Leo's car park. Each of them had a window broken. One had its tyres slashed. Three had the paintwork scratched badly. The damage occurs between about 10 p.m. and 6 a.m. I can tell you the names and addresses of a couple of louts who hang out there if you're interested.

2 You ought to investigate a house in Lufton Road. It's number 39 There's something fishy going on there. It's been empty for about six months, but recently the lights have been on and I've seen a lot of people coming and going with huge boxes at all hours of the day. There are often five or six lorries parked in the road at a time. There's a problem with burglary in our area at the moment. Perhaps the house is being used to store stolen goods.

Unit 12 Writing a summary

🔑 Key idea

A summary is a re-telling in a shorter number of words of something you have read or heard.
- Summaries require writing in complete sentences.
- Summaries should include the main idea and important points only.

One-word summaries

In each case, give one word that summarises the group of words below. *(10 marks)*

1. a place where water is stored so that it can be sent to homes
   _____

2. walking along slowly and hardly lifting the feet off the ground
   _____

3. a long hole through a hill, often for a railway line
   _____

4. a place where people can keep their money and earn interest
   _____

5. a man or woman who looks after sick or injured people
   _____

6. wet stuff that comes trickling down from the clouds
   _____

7. biting and biting and biting (when the food is tough)
   _____

8. not liking to be delayed or kept waiting for anything
   _____

9. taken into custody (by a police officer)
   _____

10. in a way showing considerable skill
    _____

22

Headlines

Make up five newspaper headlines (of not more than six words each). *(10 marks – 2 marks for each one)*

1. A mineshaft has opened under a house in a village near Durham, causing half the house to disappear down the shaft. Luckily, the owners were in the other half of the house and were not hurt – but they were shocked.

   _____

2. A large black animal, similar to a panther, has been seen by a farmer in a field near Taunton. Several sheep have been killed in the vicinity recently.

   _____

3. Cricketer Jason Foley has just scored 500 not out in a test match against Australia. He has earned a five-figure bonus for his achievement.

   _____

4. A girl, aged 12, fell at home, hit her head on a stone floor and became unconscious. Her mother dialled 999 but the ambulance did not arrive until an hour later. By that time, the girl was gravely ill. She died shortly after she was taken to hospital. Her parents were outraged and very angry at the delay.

   _____

5. A venomous spider was found in a bunch of grapes imported from South Africa. The purchaser spotted the spider and took it to a laboratory where it was examined and then killed. It was found to be extremely harmful. The store which sold the grapes has apologised and promised to inspect imports more thoroughly.

   _____

What can you remember?

Write a summary of each of the things below. Use a single sentence each time. Do not use more than twenty words in each sentence. *(10 marks – 2.5 marks for each sentence)*

1. A recent lesson which you enjoyed at school _____
   _____

2. What you did yesterday from 5 p.m. until the time you went to bed _____
   _____

3. The last television programme you watched _____
   _____

4. Your favourite book _____
   _____

Unit 13 Editing

Key idea

Editing involves reviewing and improving our own (or someone else's) writing to make it more effective.

Using more effective words

You are editing a composition written by a friend. Suggest two more effective words that could be used instead of the words in italics. Your words do not have to be synonyms of the italic words, but they should be suitable for the situation.

(10 marks – 0.5 mark for each suitable answer)

1 A group of children ran away in front of us. When we were nearly at the corner, a woman *came* out of her house. She was upset and waved her arms angrily at us.

   _____   _____

2 'Go away! Get out of here!' she *said to* us *loudly*.

   _____   _____

   _____   _____

3 The policeman *looked* at us. His face *indicated* that trouble was coming.

   _____   _____

   _____   _____

4 The old man *moved* painfully towards the receptionist.

   _____   _____

5 Mary wore a *nice* outfit to her friend's party.

   _____   _____

6 The tornado *pulled apart* the town, leaving a trail of destruction behind it.

   _____   _____

7 The poor animal *moved* towards us on its three good legs as if *asking* us to help.

   _____   _____

   _____   _____

Correcting errors

The following sentences are taken from a report by a pupil about the school canteen. Edit the sentences by correcting any mistakes in them. Write out the sentences correctly. *(10 marks – 0.5 mark for each correction)*

1 In the coarse of our investigations, we watched pupils had lunch on sevral days.

2 We noticed that some pupil had to queue a long time before they could obtained there food.

3 We therefore suggest that there should be two seperate sessions for lunch, the younger children can eat 20 minutes earlier then the oldest pupils.

4 This will also prevent the food to becoming cold and will enable the servers to work more careful, they are all in favour of this change.

5 We asked each pupil to complete a questionaire about the food, we used the information from them to produce the lists in Apendix 3

6 The tables what the pupils sit at are to crowded, so we recommend that only six pupils sit at each table, this will be possible if we have two sessions instead of one.

Using headings

(10 marks)

A classmate prepared to write a report on her school canteen. She jotted down these points:

amount of food	crowding	behaviour of pupils	servers
tables	pupil satisfaction	quality of food	cooks
cost of food	seating	cleanliness/hygiene	taste
(un)healthy food	hours/time	queues	waste

She showed you her notes and asked you for your opinion on arranging the points.

1 Suggest **five** main headings under which most or all of the points can be put.

   _____
   _____
   _____
   _____
   _____

The pupils in Miss Wilson's class asked her if they could have a class picnic, so she asked them to plan the arrangements for a picnic. One pupil wrote about the following points but did not put them under any headings or in any clear order.

date	bus/car/train/coach	music/songs	weather – alternative indoors
times	food	drinks	parents – inform, come?
place	games	cost	activities

2 Suggest **five** main headings for a plan for the picnic.

   _____
   _____
   _____
   _____
   _____

Unit 14
Conditional sentences

🔑 Key idea

A conditional sentence says that one thing depends on another. Conditional sentences usually contain the words **if** or **unless**. The "if" or "unless" part of the sentence is a special type of subordinate clause called a **conditional clause**.

      conditional clause   main clause

If you tickle me, I will laugh.

What happens?

Complete these sentences in any sensible way. They are about habitual (usual) actions. *(10 marks – 2 marks for each correct sentence)*

1 If you leave ice out of a fridge, _____

2 If a player hits another player during a game of football, _____
_____

3 If people find that they have mice in their home, _____
_____

4 If it rains while the sun is shining, _____

5 If I'm very thirsty during the night, _____

What will probably happen?

Put in the right form of the verbs in brackets. The sentences are about things that may, can or probably will happen in future. *(5 marks – 0.5 mark for each correct answer)*

1 If a young child _____ (play) with matches at home, he or she _____ (start) a fire.

2 If it rains on Saturday, our Sports Day _____ (postpone). Then it _____ (hold) on 23 June.

3 If you _____ (eat) too much food, you _____ (put) on weight.

4 If you both stand on that table at the same time, it _____ (probably collapse) and you _____ (break) something.

5 If the rain doesn't stop soon, all this area _____ (flood) and we _____ (force) to leave our home.

Giving advice

We can use *If I were you ...* to give advice:

If I were you,	I wouldn't eat so much.
	I wouldn't bother to answer that email.
	I would be honest about it.

What advice can you give these friends or relatives? *(10 marks – 2 marks for each suitable answer)*

1   Dave says he always feels tired in the morning. He admits that he rarely goes to bed before 11 p.m. because his parents let him stay up to watch films.

   _____
   _____

2   You are visiting an aunt with your brother or sister. You have both been offered a cup of coffee, but you have declined the coffee politely. Your brother or sister is not sure whether or not to try drinking it and asks your advice.

   _____
   _____

3   A friend says she has several unwanted jigsaw puzzles at home. She is not sure whether to take them to a charity shop or just to throw them away. What do you advise?

   _____
   _____
   _____

4   A friend's family are going to spend a few days in Paris during the holidays. They can't decide whether to go by rail, ferry or air. Your friend mentioned this to you and said, "What would you do?"

   _____
   _____

5   A friend goes to a different school from yours. He tells you that he has noticed that two older boys are bullying younger pupils and making them pay money nearly every day. He is not sure what, if anything, he should do. He has asked for your advice. What do you suggest?

   _____
   _____

Other ways of showing a condition

We can also show a condition by making sentences like these:

You can go	provided that	you return before dark.
You can play with them	as long as	you're back by 7.00 p.m.
It's all right for you to go	on condition that	you are not late home again.

Use the information in each pair of sentences to make one sentence using one of the connectives in the second column above. You can change, omit or add words.
(5 marks)

1. You can go to Tom's house. You must be back here by 8.00 p.m.

2. You can borrow my bike. You must return it on Saturday.

3. Tom can stay with us for the weekend. His parents must agree.

4. I'll help you. Don't argue all the time.

5. We can have a picnic on Saturday. The weather must be fine then.

Narrative writing

 **Key idea** •

The purpose of a narrative text is to tell a story. Although individual stories can be very different, they all have some common structural and language features.

Zangram by C. J. Salter: extract 1 • • • • • • • • • • •

Read this extract from *Zangram*. Then answer the questions below. *(10 marks)*

> 1   The Logan family pulled wearily into a deserted car park not far from Stonehenge. Jack Logan, exhausted after driving for nine hours, said to his wife, "I need a rest."
>
>   "Good idea," his wife replied. "I told Sylvia we wouldn't be down 'til
> 5 noon."
>
>   Jack Logan glanced in the rear-view mirror. His children, Daniel and Claire, were sleeping soundly. So he settled down and was soon asleep himself.
>
>   Some time later, Claire stirred. The car seemed to be moving, but then
> 10 the movement stopped. She heard her dad snoring contentedly, and drifted back to sleep.
>
>   On board Spacecraft 462, the doors closed and a message flashed back to Zangram, far beyond Earth's solar system: "Mission completed. 20 specimens including four bipeds in a metal shell." The spaceship rose silently
> 15 from a field near Stonehenge and hurtled off into space. It carried with it the Logan family, their car, two inquisitive dogs, a deeply resentful cat and other specimens destined for examination and display in the Zangram national zoo.

1   In paragraph one, which word repeats the idea expressed by "wearily"? *(1 mark)*

_____

2   What were Mrs Logan's exact words when she spoke to Sylvia? *(1 mark)*

_____

3   What is missing before "Good idea" (line 4)? Why has it been left out? *(2 marks)*

_____

4 What adverb could we use instead of each of the following? (The adverb need not have the same meaning as the given word, but it must fit the situation.) *(4 marks)*

   a) soundly (line 7) _____   c) silently (line 14) _____

   b) contentedly (line 10) _____   d) deeply (line 16) _____

5 a) What does "inquisitive" tell us about the dogs? b) Why was the cat "resentful"? *(2 marks)*

   _____

Zangram: extract 2

Read this continuation of *Zangram*. Then answer the questions about it.
(10 marks)

```
1   When the Logan family woke up, they discovered they were in a huge
    glass dome. They were unaware, however, of the battery of tests and
    examinations that the Zangrams had carried out on them over a period of
    several days.
5     Outside the dome, a crowd of Zangrams watched the family through
    one-way glass. A notice outside the dome said, when translated into English,
    "On loan from Planet 264S/36 for 30 days". Of course, the Logans knew
    nothing of this. They believed that somehow they had been kidnapped.
      "Well, at least we're alive," said Mrs Logan, trying to console her
10  children. "Sooner or later, we'll find out where we are and why we're here."
      She was right. They found out the next day when the Zangrams had
    finally solved the riddle of Earth language and began to communicate with
    them.
```

1 What happened to the Logan family before they were put on display? *(2 marks)*

   _____

2 Why does the writer start a new paragraph in three places after the first paragraph? Give a reason why each of the three paragraphs has been started. *(3 marks)*

   _____

   _____

   _____

3 How does the phrase that begins the second paragraph link it to the first paragraph? *(2 marks)*

   _____

4 What does the pronoun "this" in line 8 refer to? *(1 mark)*

_____

5 How does the writer create a dramatic effect at the beginning of the last paragraph? *(2 marks)*

_____

Zangram: extract 3

Now read extract 3 and answer the questions about it. *(10 marks)*

> 1   When the Logans woke up in the car park at Stonehenge, they were puzzled to find their car turned round. They knew something odd had happened, but what? They drove on to Cornwall in some confusion. Their bewilderment deepened when they finally reached the home of Jack's brother and rang the
> 5   doorbell. Tony Logan opened the door and stared at them in a mixture of astonishment and horror.
>   "Where have you been?" he said at last. "We were expecting you a month ago! We checked with your neighbours. We even informed the police because …"
> 10 "A month ago!" echoed Jack Logan. "We agreed July 10th and here we are."
>   Tony stared at his brother, trying to decide whether he was joking or not. "But today is August 10th," he pointed out. "Anyway, come in. You're welcome at any time – even when you're officially 'missing, presumed dead'."
>   Mrs Logan and the children went in. Jack went back to the car to unpack
> 15 the luggage. What he saw in the boot proved that something very strange had occurred.

1 What is similar about the ways in which extracts 1, 2 and 3 end? *(2 marks)*

_____

2 "We even informed the police because …" Why does the author insert …? *(1 mark)*

_____

3 Find five *different* uses of capital letters in the extract. *(5 marks)*

_____

_____

4 Write a sentence saying what Mr Logan found in the boot. *(2 marks)*

_____

unit 17 Describing past events

Key idea

The purpose of writing a recount is to tell about a past event. Recount texts have some common structural and language features that help to identify them.

Time connectives

Read the account of a football match below. Put in ten different linking words or expressions. Choose from those below. *(10 marks)*

right up to the final whistle	shortly afterwards	at the start of the game
within the first ten minutes	ten minutes later	for the rest of the first half
during the half-time break	at half-time	ten minutes from the end
	immediately	

(1)_____ yesterday, Newtown were confidently expected to beat Oldtown by at least two goals. Newtown forced two corners (2)_____, but failed to score. Oldtown struck back but Jordan's shot was wide. (3)_____, Ken Teale put Newtown one up when he headed home a cross from Ojuro. Play was restricted to the centre of the field (4)_____ with Newtown slightly superior. (5)_____ the score remained Newtown 1 – Oldtown 0

Newtown manager, Joe Kellick, gave his men a pep-talk (6)_____. The players responded with raids on the Oldtown goal, during which Ken Teale scored his second goal. (7)_____ Oldtown veteran, Paul Cranston, scored for Oldtown. Stung by this unexpected goal, Newtown launched another series of attacks (8)_____ and were rewarded when Ojuro scored Newtown's third goal.

(9)_____ Tom Baxter shot wide for Oldtown. Defences dominated the game (10)_____.

Final score: Newtown 3 – Oldtown 1

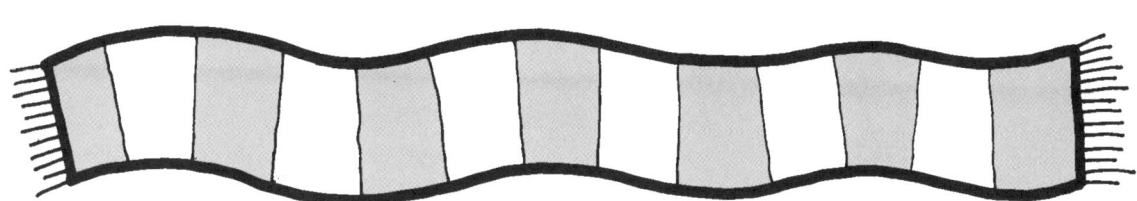

33

Exploring language

Read 'Hot water' and then answer the questions about it. *(20 marks)*

Hot water

1   Sue went to visit her grandfather, aged 90, in a remote rural district. Grandad cooked a very tasty lunch. However, when Sue put the plates and cutlery on the table, she noticed some tiny brown specks on her plate. She studied the plate thoughtfully for a few moments.

5   "Grandad," she asked hesitantly. "Are you … Are these plates clean?"

"Of course they are," Grandad replied quickly. "They're as clean as hot water can get them. That's for sure. Enjoy your meal and don't worry about the plates."

In the evening, Sue helped Grandad to prepare supper. She was hungry and
10   was just about to put the food on the plates when she saw a thin piece of something on one of the plates. It looked like scrambled egg.

"Grandad," she said firmly. "Are you absolutely sure these plates are clean?"

"No doubt about it," Grandad said with a smile. "They're as clean as hot
15   water can make them. I can guarantee that."

A few minutes later, a neighbour approached Grandad's house. Immediately his dog started to bark furiously. Grandad shouted angrily at the dog, "Cut that out, Hotwater! No more barking! Go and lay down! It's only Jim. You know him."

20   "I call her 'Hotwater'," Grandad explained to Sue, "because she always gets me into trouble."

"Ugh!" Sue thought. "I wonder if … I think I've been had."

"Grandad," she said quietly, "I'll wash the dishes tonight."

1   a) Underline any ten adjectives in the passage. *(5 marks)*

    b) Choose six of the adjectives and give words opposite in meaning to them. *(3 marks)*

    _____   _____

    _____   _____

    _____   _____

2   Choose three verbs used in the past tense in the passage. Write them down and then write the present and future tenses of each. *(3 marks)*

    _____

    _____

    _____

3   At the end of the third sentence, what one word can we insert after "plate" to turn the following sentence into a subordinate clause? _____ *(1 mark)*

4   Suggest a reason why Sue was hesitant when she first asked Grandad if the plates were clean? *(1 mark)*

    _____

5   Complete the sentence. *(1 mark)*

    "In line 6, the writer uses 'as … as' to_____

6   a) Write down any six adverbs in the passage. *(3 marks)*

    _____   _____

    _____   _____

    _____   _____

    b) Choose any four of the adverbs and write down words opposite in meaning to them. *(2 marks)*

7   What did Sue mean when she said, "I think I've been had"? *(1 mark)*

    _____

35

unit 18 Giving instructions

Key idea

Instructions, directions and descriptions of procedures all have to be written clearly and concisely so they are easy to follow. Features such as sequenced and numbered steps, imperative verbs and sequencing connectives are common to this type of writing.

Checklist

Paul wrote the following checklist for maintaining his bike. Read it and then answer the questions about it. *(15 marks)*

> Checklist for maintaining bicycles
> 1 Check <u>brake</u> cables. Do brake blocks make good contact with rims of wheels?
> 2 Is <u>bell</u> fastened firmly? Does it work properly?
> 3 Check if front and rear <u>lights</u>. Replace battry or check dynamo if necessary.
> 4 <u>Chain</u> – tighten and see if any oil is needed.
> 5 <u>Saddle</u> – make sure it is at the right height and comfortable.
> 6 <u>Carrier</u> – check that nuts holding carrier are not lose. Tighten?
> 7 Check nuts holding <u>wheels</u> in place. Tighten or replace if necessary.
> 8 Check air in <u>tyres</u>; check for slow punctures.
> 9 Grease or oil any points that need lubricating, e.g. wheel <u>axils</u>.
> 10 Check that <u>tyre valves</u> are working properly.
> 11 Buy <u>padlock</u> with at least two keys. Get extra keys cut?

1 In step 2, are "firmly" and "properly" adjectives or adverbs?
_____ *(2 marks)*

2 In step 3, what words are missing from the first sentence?
_____ *(2 marks)*

3 How could Paul do step 5? _____ *(2 marks)*

4 Find four misspelt words and correct them. *(4 marks)*

_____ _____

_____ _____

5 Rewrite step 2 as a single statement with an imperative verb. *(2 marks)*

_____

6   Which two steps could you combine so that there are only ten steps? *(2 marks)*

7   What is the purpose of step 11? *(1 mark)*

Defrosting a freezer

Rewrite Gran's instructions for how to defrost a freezer. Set them out in the right order using no more than ten steps. Leave out points that are not necessary.
(15 marks)

> Well, of course, you have to make sure that you don't make a mess in the kitchen. We don't want any water left on the floor to make the place slippery. That's how Grandad broke a leg a few years ago. Get a few old towels (there are plenty at the bottom of the airing-cupboard) and take them to the freezer. Oh, yes, you'll need a pail or a saucepan to put the water in. Put one of the towels on the floor in front of the freezer to catch the drips. Now, where was I? Ah, yes, empty the freezer. There are only a couple of packets in it now. Stick them in the fridge. Turn off the electricity. Open the freezer wide. Put a couple of towels inside to soak up the water. If you're in a hurry, put a bowl of hot water on a shelf in the freezer. It will help to thaw out the ice. You can poke any pieces of ice free if you like but it's not necessary.
>
> Leave the freezer door open and just be patient. When the ice has all gone, wring out the towels. Clean and dry the freezer. Get rid of any water. Then put the packets back in the freezer and turn it on. Easy!

Unit 19 Writing reports

Key idea

Report texts present information on a subject. They describe things as they are. They often feature present-tense verbs, descriptive adjectives and adverbs, and headings and subheadings.

The breakfast report

(10 marks)

1 "Write a report about breakfast in your family," said the teacher to Paul's class. If you were in the class, how would you arrange your ideas? Think of headings for three paragraphs. *(3 marks)*

_____

_____

_____

Breakfast by Paul

We have three different kinds of breakfast, classified according to how it is eaten.

My favourite is a "sitting-down" breakfast. It is a leisurely event on Saturday and Sunday because I do not have to get up early. It includes cereal, fried eggs, beans, mushrooms, toast and jam and a big glass of orange juice.

A "standing-up" breakfast involves a drink, toast and a piece of fruit. I usually have this on school days because I have less time.

When I forget to set the alarm and am late for school, I have to have an "on-the-move" breakfast. I shoot out of the house, buy a chocolate bar and eat it before the bell rings.

---

2 Write paragraph headings for Paul's report above. *(3 marks)*

_____

_____

_____

3 What part of speech is each of these words as it is used in Paul's report? *(4 marks)*
   a) classified _____ b) leisurely _____
   c) usually _____ d) shoot _____

38

The rodent report

This is part of a report on squirrels, written by Sally, age 11 Read it and then answer the questions about it. *(10 marks)*

Grey squirrels

Where they came from

Grey squirrels were brought to Britain from America many years ago and kept in zoos. Some excaped and spread to both rural and urban areas. They have now driven red squirrels away.

_____

They prefer to eat seeds, berries and especially nuts, so they can often be found near oak, beech and other nut trees. However, they also eat birds' eggs and baby birds. Therefore, the presents of squirrels often leads to the absence of birds since they cannot nest safely.

How they behave

Grey squirrels are active during the day and do not hibernate in winter. They are naturaly shy, but not when it comes to food. In some towns, squirrels in parks are so tame that they will take peanuts, if offered, from people's hands.

The problems they cause

Grey squirrels (in fact, all kinds of squirrels) can be pests. They raid berries and other fruit from bushes and trees in poeple's gardens. They also gnaw and eat bark, which leads to the death of trees.

---

1. a) Circle the passive verb in the first paragraph. *(1 mark)*
   b) Why is the verb not active? *(1 mark)* _____

2. Fill in the missing subheading for the second paragraph. *(2 marks)*

3. Draw a box around each of the connectives in the second paragraph. (Do not include "and".) *(2 marks)*

4. Find the four misspelled words in the report. Draw a line through each one and write the correctly spelled word above. *(2 marks)*

5. In the last sentence of the third paragraph, underline the main clause once and the subordinate clause twice. *(2 marks)*

Write a worm report

(10 marks)

Here are some notes about worms.
1 Think of four different headings under which you could group the notes.
2 Then write a four-paragraph report using the notes.

- Do not like light
- Eat dead leaves and soil
- Has complete digestive system
- Help plants to grow
- Live underground
- Long, soft bodies with head and tail end
- Make tunnels to move about
- No bones, eyes, legs
- Soil leaves body making worm "casts"
- Useful creatures – tunnels bring air to soil
- Use muscles and hairs on skin to move
- Take nutrients from soil as it passes through body

WORMS

Paragraph 1 heading:_____

Paragraph 2 heading:_____

Paragraph 3 heading:_____

Paragraph 4 heading:_____

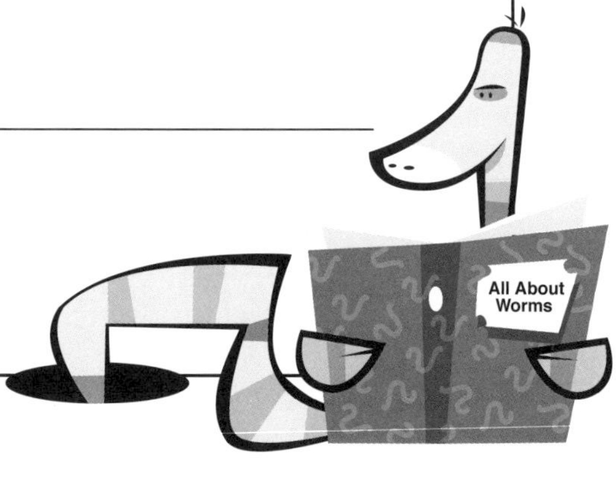

Unit 20 Persuasive writing

Key idea

Persuasive writing aims to influence the reader towards a particular opinion. It often uses emotional words, figurative devices and imperative verbs.

Email scam

Mrs Stone received this email, which is full of mistakes. Fortunately, she knew it was not from her bank at all, but an attempt by someone to find out her details illegally. Read it and answer the questions. *(10 marks)*

```
Subject: Confirm your details to avoid immediate cancellation to your
account.
Yesterday the bank have a failure of its software this resulted in a
lost of customer data. To help you to avoid from fraud, kindly connect
with the link below to confirm your account registration data, this is
obligatory to protect your account.
Please do not answer to this message. Fill in the form "Confirmation
of Acount Details".
```

1 Which words in the "subject" are meant to frighten the receiver? *(1 mark)*

2 Find an incorrect verb tense. Explain why it is wrong and correct it. *(2 marks)*

3 Find two places where punctuation is wrong or missing. Correct them. *(2 marks)*

4 Find and correct four expressions in which prepositions are used wrongly. *(2 marks)*

5 Find and correct two spelling mistakes. *(2 marks)*

6 Why does the sender of the email put in the sentence, "This is obligatory to protect your account"? *(1 mark)*

**The mighty T-watch is here:
hep, handy, helpful!**

It's COOL and it could be yours!

On one side, it's a watch.
No need to look at it.

Press the button and it tells you the time. Now that's really something – but there's more!

On the other side? A nifty recorder. Up to 10 minutes talktime. No need to take notes.

**Move up to the in-crowd!
ORDER NOW
before they're all snapped up.**

"I love it!" says pop star Kati Lane.

Football legend, Mike O'Shea: "I wouldn't be without mine!"

An advertisement

Read the advertisement above and then answer these questions. *(10 marks)*

1   Which slang words in the advertisment mean "up-to-date, fashionable"? *(1 mark)*

2   What figurative device is used in the second line? *(1 mark)*

3   Why is "COOL" put in capital letters? *(1 mark)*

4   "On the other side? A nifty recorder." Explain why the writer doesn't use complete sentences. *(2 marks)*

5   Why does the advertiser use the word "nifty" instead of "clever"? *(1 mark)*

6   Explain the purpose of the pictures. *(2 marks)*

7   Give one example each of two different verb forms used in the advertisement. *(1 mark)*

8   In the first draft of this advertisement, the advertiser wrote : "Keep up with the in-crowd". Why did she change this to "Move up to the in-crowd"? *(1 mark)*

Getting involved

Miss Benson's class wrote to their local council following three traffic accidents near their school. Read their first draft below and then answer the questions.
(10 marks)

> In the passed six months, there have been three horrific traffic acidents near our school, each time somebody was knocked down by a speeding motorist. We beg the Council to do something to make Bridge Street safer.
>
> We would like to recommend four crucial measures. First of all, we hope the Council can put some speed bumps in the road to slow down traffic. Secondly, we need a pedestran crossing outside our school. Thirdly, it would be a good idea to errect warning sines at each end of Bridge Street, finally, we think that cars should not be aloud to park outside our school for longer than 15 minutes during 8–9 a.m. and 3–4 p.m. on school days.

1. Why do the children mention accidents in their letter? *(1 mark)*

2. Give two examples of powerful, emotive words in the letter. Why do the children use them? *(2 marks)*

3. Find and correct six spelling mistakes in the draft letter. *(3 marks)*

4. Find two places where a comma should be replaced by a full stop. *(1 mark)*

5. Find a passive verb in the first paragraph. *(1 mark)*

6. List the sequencing connectives used in the second paragraph. *(1 mark)*

7. How might the children revise the layout of the second paragraph so that their suggestions are clearer? *(1 mark)*

Unit 21: Writing discussion texts

Key idea

Discussion texts give a balanced presentation of all the various positions that are held about an issue or topic – for example, both sides of an argument.

Television: points of view

"Does television do more harm than good?" Read the first draft of what one pupil wrote and then answer the questions about it. *(10 marks)*

1   Most television shows have a bad influence to viewers, especially young ones. They use swear words and bad language most of the time. Violence is common in "soaps" and are regarded as a model or example to teenagers.

    On the other hand, documentries are both educational and intresting. There is always
5   something new for viewers to learn as long as they can stay awake. Oddly enough, the cartoons are usually OK. They are always amusing without setting a bad example. Sports programmes are also worth watching and do not cause no harm or offence.

    Maybe the only fair answer to the question is that the affect of TV depends upon the individual. If you have firm principals, you can always chose wisely. I hope that television
10 channels will clean up their act, but I won't hold my breathe waiting for that to happen.

1 What more accurate word should the writer use instead of "most" in lines 1 and 2? *(1 mark)*

2 In lines 1 and 3, replace "to" with correct prepositions. *(2 marks)*

3 Explain and correct the error of agreement in the third sentence. *(1 mark)*

4 Explain and correct the error in the last sentence of the second paragraph. *(1 mark)*

5 Correct six spelling mistakes in the last two paragraphs. *(3 marks)*

6 Is the writer's discussion well-balanced? Explain your answer. *(2 marks)*

Maths – or no maths?

"Should children be allowed to decide whether they want to study maths or not?" Read the first draft of what one pupil wrote and then answer the questions about it. *(10 marks)*

1   Some people say that we do not need maths in our daily lifes because calculaters and computers can give us all the answers. I don't agree to that because sometimes if we don't know any maths it is easy for crooks to cheat us. Also we need maths whenever we buy or sell anything and maybe we have no calculator available.

5   On the other hand, it is true that algebra and geometry can be too difficult to some children and they become confused and fed up. Then they may even hate the subject and start to behave badly at school. Perhaps the right thing to do is to make basic maths compulsery up to, say, the age of 14 and to make it optional after that. If somebody is no good at maths (even when he or she tries very hard), it is a waist of time to force the
10 person to continue to study the subject.

1 Find and correct four spelling errors: two in each paragraph *(2 marks)*

2 Correct the mistakes in the use of prepositions in lines 2 and 5 *(1 mark)*

3 What more formal words could the writer use instead of "crooks" (line 3) and "fed up" (line 6)? *(1 mark)*

4 How many points for each side of the argument does the writer give? What are they? *(4 marks)*

5 Do you agree with the writer's conclusion? Give reasons for your answer. *(2 marks)*

Should it be a crime to kill any wild animal?

(10 marks)

Put a suitable word in each blank space. *(7 marks – 0.5 mark for each correct answer)*

I am in favour of protecting wild animals, but there (1)_____ two main reasons (2)_____ I do not think it (3)_____ be a crime to kill any wild animal. Firstly, sometimes it is (4)_____ to kill wild animals such as mice, rats and rabbits. (5)_____ we do not kill some of them, they will increase (6)_____ cause serious problems. A (7)_____ reason is that sometimes wild animals, such (8)_____ boars, foxes, badgers and deer, increase and (9)_____ a threat to farmers. Then it is necessary to kill some of (10)_____.

We must also remember (11)_____ some farmers keep cattle, sheep, deer, goats and (12)_____ animals for their milk or meat. Are these wild animals? If somebody kills a wild pony on Dartmoor (13)_____ that a crime? As I said earlier, I think some wild animals should be protected, but making it a crime to kill one is not the (14)_____ way of doing it.

- **Do you think it should be a crime to kill wild animals? Give two reasons for your answer.** *(3 marks)*

_____
_____
_____
_____
_____

unit 22

Investigating English expressions

 **Key idea** ....

Investigating language is the best way to find out how it works.

American English ....

(16 marks)

Americans speak English, but many of their words differ from British English. Do you know what they're talking about? Put the right British word by each American word below. *(8 marks – 0.5 mark for each correct answer)*

| taxi   pavement   sweets   dummy (for a baby)   nappy   trousers |
| autumn   boot (of a car)   lorry   curtains   petrol   sweet biscuits |
| lift   handbag   queue   tap (for water) |

1 cab _____

2 line _____

3 fall _____

4 truck _____

5 diaper _____

6 purse _____

7 candy _____

8 pants _____

9 trunk (of a car) _____

10 gas(oline) _____

11 pacifier _____

12 cookies _____

13 faucet _____

14 sidewalk _____

15 drapes _____

16 elevator _____

Now find out for yourself the British words for these American words. *(8 marks)*

17 drugstore _____

18 closet _____

19 stove _____

20 hood (of a car) _____

21 vacation _____

22 garbage _____

23 movies _____

24 buck (money) _____

47

Investigating idioms

Put the right idiom on each line below. *(14 marks)*

- a Tartar
- eyewash
- a close shave
- a mouthpiece
- a square peg in a round hole
- a rough diamond
- a pig in a poke
- a fool's paradise
- a blank cheque
- a fly in the ointment
- a red herring
- a hornets' nest
- soft soap
- a white lie

1 A _____ is an untrue statement which is made for good reasons, for example to protect an innocent person.

2 _____ is something (usually a statement) meant to deceive people or hide something wrong.

3 _____ is a person who is very difficult to deal with even if you have some advantage over them. Many years ago, if you captured this person in a battle, he would prove a troublesome prisoner.

4 _____ is something which is meant to deceive you, perhaps by making you look in the wrong direction when trying to solve a problem.

5 _____ is permission to do as you like, for example to spend as much money as you like because the cheque has been signed but no amount has been put in.

6 If you spend a lot of time dreaming about winning a lottery, you may live in _____, thinking about something nice which will never happen.

7 If you buy _____, you buy something (such as a pig tied up in a sack) before you have had a chance to inspect it.

8 _____ is flattery.

9 _____ is somebody who appears tough or lacking in manners, but is really very kind and generous.

10 If a person is in a job that does not suit him or her, we may say that the person is _____.

11 _____ is an obstacle to a plan.

12 Sometimes we call a narrow escape _____.

13 _____ is somebody who speaks on behalf of another person or organisation, often to give excuses or reasons for an action.

14 _____ is a source of possible trouble because if you interfere you may create a worse situation.

Key Grammar is a brand new resource, specifically planned to cover all the key grammar objectives in self-contained units of work. The pupil books feature:

- clear, progressive units covering all key learning objectives
- plenty of practice and consolidation work
- opportunities to challenge and extend children's learning
- a clear mark scheme
- exercises in an appropriate context, with engaging illustrations

The workbooks provide activities for additional practice, differentiation, and homework. The important language skills coverage in **Key Grammar** is complemented by two associated series: **Key Comprehension** and **Key Spelling** – up-to-date and engaging resources which reinforce key teaching points and enable children to practise, consolidate and extend their learning. For further information about **Key Comprehension** and **Key Spelling** call our Customer Services Department on **(+44) (0)1865 888000**.

Author: Alan Etherton

Ginn is an imprint of Pearson education Limited, a company incorporated in England and Wales, having its registered office at Edinburgh Gate, Harlow, Essex, CM20 2JE.
Registered company number: 872828

www.ginn.co.uk
Help and support for teachers plus the widest range of education solutions

© Harcourt Education Limited 2005

This book is copyright and reproduction of the whole or part without the publishers' written permission is prohibited.

Key Grammar Workbook 4
ISBN: 978 0602 20685 7
Level 4 Easy Order Pack: 978 0602 20651 2
Level 4 Workbook 6 Pack: 978 0602 20648 2

First published 2005

16
13

Cover illustration by Pet Gotohda
Cover design by Tom Cole
Designed by Nicki Wise, Te Marama Design
Illustrations by David Semple, Gary Swift, Andrew Painter

Printed and bound in China (GCC/13)

Grammar Workbook 4

Contents

Unit 1	Word classes	page 2
Unit 2	Using standard English	page 4
Unit 3	Active and passive verbs 1	page 6
Unit 4	Connectives	page 8
Unit 5	Forming complex sentences 1	page 10
Unit 6	Punctuation	page 12
Unit 8	Active and passive verbs 2	page 14
Unit 9	Official language	page 16
Unit 10	Forming complex sentences 2	page 18
Unit 11	Making notes	page 20
Unit 12	Writing a summary	page 22
Unit 13	Editing	page 24
Unit 14	Conditional sentences	page 27
Unit 16	Narrative writing	page 30
Unit 17	Describing past events	page 33
Unit 18	Giving instructions	page 36
Unit 19	Writing reports	page 38
Unit 20	Persuasive writing	page 41
Unit 21	Writing discussion texts	page 44
Unit 22	Investigating English expressions	page 47

Unit 1: Word classes

Key idea

Words are categorised in classes according to the jobs they do in a sentence: noun, pronoun, verb, adjective, adverb, preposition, conjunction and interjection. Words can belong to more than one class.

Work it out

Give one-word answers. *(10 marks)*

1. Which proper noun is the name of the Italian capital? _____
2. Which adjective is the opposite of "wise"? _____
3. Which collective noun means "a lot of (birds flying) together"? _____
4. Which verb means "to tremble with cold or fear"? _____
5. Which pronoun is the opposite of "no one"? _____
6. Which proper noun is the name of the shortest month of the year? _____
7. Which adverb is the opposite of "rarely"? _____
8. What is the second part of the conjunction "not only…"? _____
9. What adverb can we form from "skill"? _____
10. Which verb means to "make longer"? _____

Which word?

Ring or underline the right word in the brackets. *(10 marks)*

1. It was dark, so we couldn't see (nothing, anything) clearly.
2. Would you mind (to wait, waiting) a few minutes?
3. There (are, is) more than one way of solving this problem.
4. Where (are, is) the rest of the players?
5. The change in the plan will not have a great deal of (affect, effect) on us.
6. Don't be so (impatience, impatient), John!
7. Between you and (I, me), I think Margaret is quite right to be suspicious.
8. This photo is different (than, from) that one.
9. We watched the marathon, but we did not (took, take) part in it.
10. Your new bike is much better than (Paul's, Pauls').

Classify it

Read this passage from *Nicholas Nickleby* by Charles Dickens. Place each of the underlined words under the correct heading in the grid below. *(10 marks – 0.5 mark for each correctly placed word)*

Dotheboy's Hall <u>was</u> not a hall at all, <u>but</u> a bare and dirty room with a <u>couple</u> of windows, in which most of the glass was broken. There were a few old <u>rickety</u> desks, <u>cut</u> and notched, and inked and damaged, in <u>every</u> possible way; a detached desk for <u>Squeers</u>; and another <u>for</u> his assistant. The ceiling was supported, like <u>that</u> of a barn, by cross beams and rafters; and the walls were so stained that it was impossible to tell <u>whether</u> they had ever been painted or whitewashed.

But the pupils! How his last hopes <u>faded</u> as <u>he</u> looked <u>around</u>! Pale and haggard faces of old men, boys of stunted growth, and others whose long thin legs would <u>hardly</u> carry their <u>stooping</u> bodies, all <u>crowded</u> together; there were the bleary eye, the hare-lip, the crooked foot, and every problem arising from <u>cruelty</u> and neglect. There were little faces which should have been handsome, darkened with the scowl of suffering; there were vicious-faced boys, brooding like prisoners in jail; <u>and</u> there were children <u>who</u> were weeping <u>with</u> loneliness…

nouns	
pronouns	
verbs	
adjectives	
adverbs	
prepositions	
conjunctions	

Unit 2 Using standard English

Key idea

We can use non-standard English in speech, but we must use standard English in formal written work.

Does it agree?

Underline the subject each time. (It may be a single word or a group of words.) Then circle the right word in the brackets so that the verb agrees with its subject.
(14 marks)

1 How much of the information in newspaper reports or radio and television news reports (are, is) completely accurate?

2 According to a report on television, a reward of several thousand pounds (has, have) been offered for information leading to the arrest of the robbers.

3 The driver of the bus – together with two of the passengers – (was, were) slightly injured in the accident.

4 (Is, Are) there any mud on your shoes?

5 The number of flights from London to Spain (have, has) risen in recent years because more people like to spend a holiday on the Spanish coast.

6 There (is, are) a number of reasons why people prefer to spend their holiday abroad. The main attraction is the better climate overseas.

7 What a nuisance! All the traffic (has, have) stopped. There must have been an accident somewhere ahead of us.

8 Before the play started, a member of the cast peeped through the curtains and said, "Oh, good! The audience (is, are) a really big one tonight. There are no empty seats."

9 Everybody in our class (want, wants) to join in the picnic, don't they?

10 How long (has, have) all this rubbish been lying here?

11 As a result of a change in the law, the poor (is, are) likely to be better off.

12 A good standard of numeracy (is, are) necessary in many jobs.

13 At least a third of those players (is, are) from foreign countries.

14 The majority of the pupils in our class (does, do) not come to school in a car.

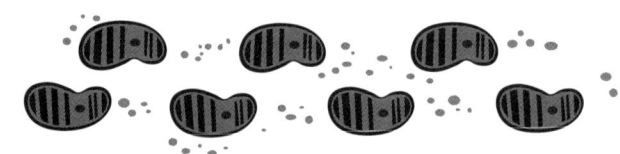

Choose the right word

Ring or underline the right words in the brackets. *(8 marks)*

1 This shop doesn't sell cosmetics (or, nor) health foods.
2 My sister doesn't like garlic and (so, nor) do I.
3 Sometimes people are not sure where to keep their money. If they hide (them, it) at home, there is always a risk of burglary.
4 The manager told his staff that he hadn't (no, any) intention of resigning.
5 John did not feel very well at the start of the cross-country race, and he felt much (worse, worser) at the end.
6 After the show, my friend and (me, I) bought some chips and ate (it, them) on the way home.
7 We need somebody to check all the electrical (equipment, equipments) before we turn on the computer and heating.
8 Our visit to Scandinavia (maybe, may be) described as a tour rather than a holiday.

Make it formal

Write more formal expressions that we can use instead of the italic words. *(8 marks)*

1 That's a *lousy* idea. _____
2 There's a rumour that their business is *on the rocks*. _____
3 All the *kids* in my class agree with me. _____
4 I haven't got *nothing* special to tell you. _____
5 The man said he didn't know *no one* with that name. _____
6 The fact that he is guilty *sticks out like a sore thumb*. _____
7 This hairstyle is gradually *catching on*. _____
8 *How come* you're not at school today? _____

Unit 3 Active and passive verbs 1

🗝 Key idea

Verbs can be in the **active** or **passive** voice.

A dangerous job

Write in the *passive* Simple Present form of the verbs in brackets. *(12 marks)*

In Malaysia, rubber (1)_____ (grow) on many estates. At dawn, rubber-tappers start work. Many of them are women and they know that their work can be dangerous. Sometimes tappers (2)_____ (attack) by a tiger. When they bend down to tap a tree, they (3)_____ (sometimes mistake) for a wild animal and attacked by a hungry tiger.

Tappers start work before the sun rises. First, a cut (4)_____ (make) in a mature tree. A tin or half a coconut shell (5)_____ (fasten) to the tree. It (6)_____ (use) to collect latex from the cut. The tapper cuts many trees. Then he or she returns to the first tree. Latex in the tin (7)_____ (empty) into a pail which (8)_____ (take) to the small "factory" on the estate. Chemicals (9)_____ (add) to the latex and mixed in well. Later on, the latex (10)_____ (squeeze) into sheets which (11)_____ (hang) in a smoke-filled hut. Finally, the sheets of rubber (12)_____ (tie) up in bales, ready for export to other countries.

A gas leak

Put in the *passive* form of the verbs in brackets. Use *has/have been* + *a past participle* each time. *(10 marks)*

One evening Mrs Wilson (Mrs W) was on her way home from work. She got off a bus and started to walk the 200 metres to her home. As she walked round a corner, she was surprised to see a crowd of people outside a wrecked house. There were fire-engines and police cars there too. Mrs Wilson's friend, Mrs Johnson (Mrs J), was in the crowd.

Mrs W: What's the matter? What's happened?

Mrs J: There was a gas leak. That house (1)_____ (wreck) completely.

Mrs W: (2)_____ anybody _____ (injure)?

Mrs J: Yes, two people (3)_____ (hurt). They (4)_____ (take) to hospital already.

Mrs W: What are the fire-engines doing here?

Mrs J: There was a small fire but it (5)_____ (bring) under control. The gas company (6)_____ (inform), so men are coming to repair the pipe. A lot of debris (7)_____ (hurl) across the road, so the windows in those houses (8)_____ (break). The people in those houses (9)_____ (evacuate). There were some elderly people in that old folks' home over there. They (10) _____ (move) to another home temporarily.

Mrs W: Is there anything we can do to help?

Mrs J: No, I don't think so.

In trouble

Put in the *passive* future form of the verbs in brackets. Use *will be + a past participle*. *(8 marks)*

Paul's friend, Mike, was sent off during a football match for hitting an opponent. Now Paul is asking his dad, a referee, what will happen to Mike.

Paul: Will Mike get into trouble?

Dad: Yes, I'm afraid he will. I'm sure he (1)_____ (charge) with hitting an opponent. Then he (2)_____ (ask) to attend a hearing before the Disciplinary Committee. He (3)_____ (tell) what he is charged with.

Paul: What will happen after that?

Dad: He (4)_____ (give) a chance to listen to the referee's report and ask any questions. Then he (5)_____ (invite) to make his statement and admit the charge or try to deny it.

Paul: I don't think he will deny it because everybody saw what happened. What will the Committee do?

Dad: Well, Mike (6)_____ (inform) of the decision in writing. It is probable that he (7)_____ (ban) for a few months. If he has a bad record, he (8)_____ (fine) as well, I should think.

Unit 4 Connectives

Key idea

Connectives are words and phrases that are used to link different parts of a text. They can join words, phrases, clauses, sentences and paragraphs.

Types of connectives

Underline the connectives in the sentences below. Then put them under the correct heading in the grid. *(10 marks)*

1. Paul decided to buy the bicycle although it was expensive.
2. We can go out when the rain stops.
3. Mary stuck a stamp on the envelope and then she posted the invitation.
4. Following my operation, I developed an infection in the wound.
5. We can go for a picnic on Saturday if the weather is good.
6. Mike can't go out to play now because he hasn't finished his homework yet.
7. You can go to London by train or you can travel on the express bus.
8. Our new house is bigger than our old one. Moreover, it has a large garden.
9. Most people like Susan, but I think she is rather conceited.
10. Despite having a terrible cold, the soprano performed her solo.

Addition	Time	Cause and effect	Opposition

Connective starters

Complete each sentence in a suitable way to show that you understand the connective. *(10 marks)*

1 We'll have to wait here until _____

2 If you eat too much, _____

3 We couldn't move the wardrobe because _____

4 Although it snowed last night, _____

5 In spite of the cold weather, _____

6 Kate is very fond of animals, so _____

7 Choose your sweets and then _____

8 I forgot to set the alarm. As a result, _____

9 The game started on time despite _____

10 I often eat fish. However, _____

Choosing connectives

Ring or underline the right word in the brackets. *(10 marks)*

1 We can go there by taxi. (Alternately, Alternatively) we can take the bus.

2 (Despite, In spite) the discount, Mrs Lee decided not to buy the car.

3 We had to leave our house when a pipe burst. Now we're waiting for the workmen to complete the repairs. In the (while, meantime), we're staying with my grandparents.

4 The team has succeeded because the owner of the club is a billionaire. (Nevertheless, Furthermore) it has one of the best managers in Europe.

5 Crocodiles have no predators to attack them. (Consequently, Subsequently) they manage to live for many years.

6 Trees can spread their seeds in many ways. (Meanwhile, For example,) sycamore seeds have "wings" to help them fly away from the parent tree.

7 We don't agree with Paul's plan. On the (other hand, contrary), we think it could be disastrous for the club.

8 His plan contains several faults. (Nevertheless, Similarly) it contains some good points.

9 You ought to buy yourself a watch (instead of, in spite of) borrowing mine.

10 Most shops have security cameras (providing, so that) they can catch thieves.

unit 5

Forming complex sentences 1

Key idea

Complex sentences are made up of more than one clause.
The clauses can be joined in different ways.

Completing sentences

**Complete these sentences in any sensible way.
Draw a ring round the connecting words.** *(10 marks)*

1 A library is a place where _____

2 There was a hidden cottage where _____

3 Don't forget to turn the lights off when _____

4 People go to a dentist when _____

5 Plants will usually grow well if _____

6 Traffic police may stop a motorist if _____

7 Mary had the flu last week, so _____

8 Paul could not hear what people were saying on television, so _____
   _____

9 You can go to your friend's house now, provided that _____
   _____

10 You can borrow my bike if you like, provided that _____
   _____

What and where?

**Complete each sentence by saying *what* people are doing and *where* they are
doing it. Start with a present participle (an –ing word)** *(10 marks)*

Example: We watched some men **repairing** a pipe in the road near our home.

1 Ashra heard two women _____

2 When I came out of my house, I noticed a man _____
   _____

3 When we reached the beach, we saw some fishermen _____
   _____

4   Before we entered the park, we stopped to watch some boys _____
   _____

5   When Sue looked out of the window, she saw a blackbird _____
   _____

6   Last night on television we watched some girls _____
   _____

7   After a few minutes, the fox came to a field and was happy to see some lambs
   _____

8   Mr Evans woke up during the night when he heard somebody _____
   _____

9   When our bus passed Mary's house, we saw her father _____
   _____

10 The lifeguard ran down the beach when he heard somebody_____
   _____

Punctuating complex sentences

Put in the missing commas. *(10 marks)*

1   Yesterday in broad daylight the police caught two men trying to rob a bank.

2   The frightened rabbit stayed absolutely still hoping that the fox had not seen it.

3   My father the manager of the store starts work before 8 a.m.

4   Last night the temperature in most Welsh towns was above freezing-point. In Aberystwyth however it was minus four degrees.

5   Did you enjoy yourself at the party last Saturday Kate?

6   Although the concert lasted for over two hours the audience was captivated by the soloist who was only ten.

7   Not having seen her cousin for several years Sue was surprised to see how tall he was.

8   Birmingham is a very large city. In fact it is one of the largest in the United Kingdom.

9   When the phone rang Peter hurried to answer it hoping that it was his friend.

10 Leaping over the wall the frightened animal disappeared into the woods.

Punctuation

Key idea

Adding clauses increases the complexity of sentences, so more punctuation is required.

Using commas

Put in commas where necessary. The sentences show various different uses of commas. *(10 marks)*

1 The home of the Duke of Devonshire has 173 rooms and houses more than 60 types of clocks.

2 Paul go and find Mary please.

3 Worms are probably the most common bait for fish. If you expect to catch fish therefore you must be prepared to handle worms.

4 'Ugh! I'm not going to touch a worm' Katie said.

5 One of our neighbours Mrs Collins is a very experienced nurse.

6 Even if I were a billionaire I would not want to live alone in a huge isolated house.

7 Very few people read poetry books in their leisure time. Many modern pop songs however contain their own type of poetry and are very popular.

8 When tadpoles get older their tails get shorter their legs get longer and they gradually develop into very small frogs.

9 Pauline Taylor whose father is a maths teacher is always top of the class in maths not surprisingly.

10 If you're ready it's time for us to leave for the airport Grandad.

Using speech marks

Each of these unpunctuated sentences contains direct speech. Rewrite them, putting in the speech marks and other punctuation marks and capital letters that are necessary. *(10 marks)*

1 My friend said to me would you mind checking this letter for me please

2 I told her you've left an r out of preferred

3 Miss Lee told me you should have written chose and not choose

4 I heard Paul shout out wait for me Mike so we waited for him

5 If you've finished your homework my mother said you can watch the film on TV

6 when the performance ended the audience rose to their feet and shouted bravo

7 clamouring up the treacherous rocks the mountain rescuer cried hold on

8 can i follow you asked grace i dont know the way besides its dark

9 the wizard whose wand was misbehaving shook his finger and said abracadabra

10 louise rubbed her eyes yawned and mumbled whats the matter

More punctuation practice

Put in any necessary punctuation marks and capital letters. *(10 marks)*

1 its the end of march tomorrow remember to put your clocks on an hour

2 remember what people say in america spring forward fall back

3 in sentence 2 the word fall means autumn

4 there are 24 children in our class 14 boys and 10 girls

5 i think that jacket is a real bargain don't you mary

6 that was my first visit to a zoo I thought it was very interesting

7 come in sit down would you like a soft drink

8 some girls like to play netball or rounders others prefer hockey

9 the speaker promised the people many things more jobs higher pay longer holidays and lower taxes

10 don't forget the saying nothing ventured nothing gained

Unit 8 Active and passive verbs 2

Key idea

Verbs can be in the **active** or **passive** voice.

Look to the future

Read the two passages. Write in the *passive* future form of the verbs in brackets.
(10 marks)

A. Tomorrow part of the motorway (1)_____ (close) for urgent resurfacing. The work (2)_____ (complete) by 4 p.m., when the road (3)_____ (reopen) to traffic. While the road is closed, traffic (4)_____ (divert). Notices (5)_____ (put) up to show motorists the route to follow.

B. Miss Harris told her class, "Our Sports Day will be on next Friday. It (6)_____ (hold) on the school field, starting at noon. All lessons will be (7)_____ (cancel) for the afternoon of that day. All parents (8)_____ (invite) to come. If bad weather is forecast, you (9)_____ (tell) and Sports Day (10)_____ (postpone) to the following week."

Will, may or must?

Read these sentences carefully. Then decide whether to put in *will*, *may* or *must*.
(10 marks)

1   This letter is urgent. It _____ be posted as soon as possible.

2   During a thunderstorm, don't shelter under a tree. It _____ be hit by lightning. If it is hit, you _____ be killed or seriously injured.

3   Be careful if you see an adder. It is a venomous snake with black zigzag marks on its top. Don't go near or touch an adder. If you do, you _____ be bitten. Then you _____ be taken to hospital. You _____ be given an antidote to fight the venom from the snake.

4 Check your bike before you go for a long ride. The brakes _____ be checked and the tyres _____ be pumped up if necessary.

5 When people return from a holiday overseas, their passports _____ be checked by an Immigration Officer. Then their luggage _____ be searched by a Customs Officer.

Active to passive

Change these sentences so that they contain *passive* verbs instead of active ones. Leave out the italic words. *(10 marks)*

1 *Somebody* stole Mr Jackson's car during the night.

2 Before the dentist drilled my tooth, *she* gave me an injection.

3 *Some workmen* pulled down that old factory last week.

4 *The strong wind* blew down two trees last night.

5 *Somebody* has just taken Mrs Sharpe to hospital.

6 *Two dustmen* collect our rubbish every Friday.

7 *People* grow a lot of apples in this part of the country.

8 *Sharks or other large fish* sometimes attack swimmers not far from the beach.

9 *The Mayor* will open the new school tomorrow.

10 *Several workmen* will redecorate our school during the holidays.

Official language

 **Key idea** •

Formal and official documents have certain language features that distinguish them from informal writing.

Informal: first person (personal); colloquial/slang vocabulary; use of contractions; short, simple sentences; exclamations, questions

Formal: third person (impersonal); technical, subject-specific vocabulary; no contractions; complex sentences; statements

Len Benton sent his friend, Mary Evans, a fake formal letter from a firm of solicitors when she wanted to borrow his bicycle. Mary decided to continue the game with Len. She sent him this invitation to her birthday party.

> On behalf of Miss Mary Evans, we have very considerable pleasure in requesting the pleasure of your company at a sumptuous festive social gathering of young attractive females and boisterous males to celebrate the eleventh anniversary of her blessed nativity.
>
> Please be informed accordingly that this joyful event will take place at Miss Evans' ancestral place of residence at 462 Rowan Road on Saturday 25 April, commencing punctually at 4 p.m. and drawing to a close by 8 p.m.
>
> To enable us to make adequate preparations, we would greatly appreciate it if you would kindly get in touch with us and indicate whether or not you will be able to join all concerned in this celebration. Kindly let us know what you decide before noon on 21 April so that our plans may be finalised well in advance. Alternatively, you may prefer to make your decision known directly to Mary (by phone, email, fax or in person).
>
> We are asked to pass on to all guests Mary's particular request that presents should not be brought or sent.

What do they mean? •

Find and underline the expressions in Mary's invitation that have these meanings.
(10 marks)

1 are happy	3 party	5 birthday	7 home	9 would like
2 to invite	4 children	6 note (verb)	8 finishing	10 everybody

In translation

Len's brother asked him what was in the letter from Mary. Pretend you are Len. Tell your brother – in everyday English – what the main points of the invitation are. *(10 marks)*

_____
_____
_____
_____
_____
_____

Keep it simple

Give the meaning of the expressions in italics. Use ordinary, everyday English that makes the meaning clear but uses fewer words. *(10 marks)*

1 Please *contact him in writing*. _____

2 Write your name here, *giving your surname and all given names*.
   _____

3 *In the event that* you are unable to come, bring a note when you recover.
   _____

4 Mike missed a lot of lessons at school *as a result* of illness.
   _____

5 Ask a parent or *the person who is legally responsible for looking after you* to write a note to your teacher, explaining why you were absent.
   _____

6 Peter cannot come today because he is *suffering from some illness*.
   _____

7 The *man who has been accused of robbery but has not yet been tried or convicted* will give evidence tomorrow.
   _____

8 Mr Macdonald is a farmer, so he would like to *wipe out and completely get rid of* all the rabbits on his farm.
   _____

9 Your claim for compensation will be *studied in detail to ascertain all aspects of the problem*.
   _____

10 You will be told *what is eventually decided by officials who look into your case*.
   _____

Unit 10 Forming complex sentences 2

Key idea

subordinate clause · main clause · subordinate clause

After the party, we all went straight home because it was late.

There are different types of subordinate clauses. They are linked to the main clause with connectives.

Adding connectives

Put one of the following connectives in each blank space below. *(10 marks)*

if	after	before	although	when	so
while	despite	provided		so	that

1 I have a poster that reminds me to wash my hands _____ I have a meal, and to clean my teeth _____ I have eaten anything.

2 _____ Mum agrees, we're going to have a barbecue this evening _____ it doesn't rain.

3 The house in Elm Street was too expensive and _____ my parents decided not to buy it _____ we all liked it very much

4 You can borrow these videos but let me have them back _____ Mary can watch them _____ she returns from holiday.

5 The fire started _____ men were carrying out repairs. It destroyed the whole building _____ the efforts of the firemen.

Punctuating complex sentences

Punctuate these sentences correctly. Don't forget to put in capital letters where necessary. *(10 marks – 2 marks for each correct sentence)*

1 we expected toms friend to come at 5 pm however he didnt arrive until 530

2 in the middle of lunch a boy rushed into the canteen shouting fire fire

3 I put my books away and turned off the light then I went to bed

4 when the phone rang maya picked it up expecting to hear her friends voice

5 the answer peter gave although partially correct was not the right one

Joining sentences

Join each group of sentences to make one sentence. You can change, add or omit words. *(10 marks – 2.5 marks for each correct sentence)*

1 The rain stopped. We played in the garden. The grass was still wet. We were quite chilly.

2 The girl won lots of money. She gave half of it to charity. She is Janet's cousin.

3 This is the ring. My aunt gave it to me. I was ten then. It is beautiful.

4 Uncle George is over fifty. He completed the marathon. He raised lots of money for charity.

Unit 11 Making notes

Key idea

We make notes to extract the most important points from written words (such as information text) or spoken words (such as a telephone conversation or interview). We write them down in a shorter form.

Babysitting

You are babysitting for Mrs Done. You receive some phone calls and need to jot down notes so that you can write out messages for her. Make notes. *(10 marks)*

1 Is that Connie Jackson? Oh, well, maybe I could leave a message for her. My name is Peter Brown. I was going to call on her tomorrow at her office at about ten but something has come up, so I can't make it. Please ask her to phone my secretary at 099-438 tomorrow to fix another appointment. Thursday or Friday would be fine for me, ideally in the morning. Thanks. Goodbye.

2 Can I interest you in a good deal on double-glazing? This week we're offering … Oh, I see. Hmmm. Well, perhaps you'd tell her that Glunk Glass have this special offer next week, for seven days only. We're offering a discount of twenty-five per cent for two windows or more. If further details are needed, ask the lady to phone Andrew Brown at 047-738 any time. Thanks.

Customer services

You are learning the work in the Customer Services Department of a busy store. People phone, so you have to take notes and then tell the manager what the complaint is about. Read what these people said to you. Make notes. *(10 marks)*

1 My name's Ivy Trott. What's that? No, I'm not related to her. What I want to do is complain about the Milky Way Mousse. Don't get me wrong. I like them very much, but you never seem to have any in stock. What's happened? Are the staff eating them all? How come you've never got any on sale? Please ask somebody to order some more, pronto!

2 I want to complain about the tomatoes in your fruit and vegetable section. I usually buy a packet of six. Twice I've found that two of the tomatoes were bad underneath. They look all right on top but when you get them out – that's a different story. Maybe you could have a word with your order clerk or whoever does the ordering and change your supplier. I'll check up on them in the coming weeks and let you know if I see any improvement. I will be bringing back the two bad ones I bought this week and will expect a refund.

Local newspaper reporter

You are a reporter in the office of a local newspaper. You receive these phone calls. Make notes of the important points. *(10 marks)*

1 In the past week, six cars have been damaged by hooligans in Leo's car park. Each of them had a window broken. One had its tyres slashed. Three had the paintwork scratched badly. The damage occurs between about 10 p.m. and 6 a.m. I can tell you the names and addresses of a couple of louts who hang out there if you're interested.

2 You ought to investigate a house in Lufton Road. It's number 39 There's something fishy going on there. It's been empty for about six months, but recently the lights have been on and I've seen a lot of people coming and going with huge boxes at all hours of the day. There are often five or six lorries parked in the road at a time. There's a problem with burglary in our area at the moment. Perhaps the house is being used to store stolen goods.

unit 12 Writing a summary

Key idea

A summary is a re-telling in a shorter number of words of something you have read or heard.
- Summaries require writing in complete sentences.
- Summaries should include the main idea and important points only.

One-word summaries

In each case, give one word that summarises the group of words below. *(10 marks)*

1. a place where water is stored so that it can be sent to homes
   _____

2. walking along slowly and hardly lifting the feet off the ground
   _____

3. a long hole through a hill, often for a railway line
   _____

4. a place where people can keep their money and earn interest
   _____

5. a man or woman who looks after sick or injured people
   _____

6. wet stuff that comes trickling down from the clouds
   _____

7. biting and biting and biting (when the food is tough)
   _____

8. not liking to be delayed or kept waiting for anything
   _____

9. taken into custody (by a police officer)
   _____

10. in a way showing considerable skill
    _____

22

Headlines

Make up five newspaper headlines (of not more than six words each). *(10 marks – 2 marks for each one)*

1   A mineshaft has opened under a house in a village near Durham, causing half the house to disappear down the shaft. Luckily, the owners were in the other half of the house and were not hurt – but they were shocked.

   _____

2   A large black animal, similar to a panther, has been seen by a farmer in a field near Taunton. Several sheep have been killed in the vicinity recently.

   _____

3   Cricketer Jason Foley has just scored 500 not out in a test match against Australia. He has earned a five-figure bonus for his achievement.

   _____

4   A girl, aged 12, fell at home, hit her head on a stone floor and became unconscious. Her mother dialled 999 but the ambulance did not arrive until an hour later. By that time, the girl was gravely ill. She died shortly after she was taken to hospital. Her parents were outraged and very angry at the delay.

   _____

5   A venomous spider was found in a bunch of grapes imported from South Africa. The purchaser spotted the spider and took it to a laboratory where it was examined and then killed. It was found to be extremely harmful. The store which sold the grapes has apologised and promised to inspect imports more thoroughly.

   _____

What can you remember?

Write a summary of each of the things below. Use a single sentence each time. Do not use more than twenty words in each sentence. *(10 marks – 2.5 marks for each sentence)*

1   A recent lesson which you enjoyed at school _____
   _____

2   What you did yesterday from 5 p.m. until the time you went to bed _____
   _____

3   The last television programme you watched _____
   _____

4   Your favourite book _____
   _____

Editing

Key idea

Editing involves reviewing and improving our own (or someone else's) writing to make it more effective.

Using more effective words

You are editing a composition written by a friend. Suggest two more effective words that could be used instead of the words in italics. Your words do not have to be synonyms of the italic words, but they should be suitable for the situation.

(10 marks – 0.5 mark for each suitable answer)

1 A group of children ran away in front of us. When we were nearly at the corner, a woman *came* out of her house. She was upset and waved her arms angrily at us.

   _____   _____

2 'Go away! Get out of here!' she *said to* us *loudly*.

   _____   _____
   _____   _____

3 The policeman *looked* at us. His face *indicated* that trouble was coming.

   _____   _____
   _____   _____

4 The old man *moved* painfully towards the receptionist.

   _____   _____

5 Mary wore a *nice* outfit to her friend's party.

   _____   _____

6 The tornado *pulled apart* the town, leaving a trail of destruction behind it.

   _____   _____

7 The poor animal *moved* towards us on its three good legs as if *asking* us to help.

   _____   _____
   _____   _____

24

Correcting errors

The following sentences are taken from a report by a pupil about the school canteen. Edit the sentences by correcting any mistakes in them. Write out the sentences correctly. *(10 marks – 0.5 mark for each correction)*

1. In the coarse of our investigations, we watched pupils had lunch on sevral days.

2. We noticed that some pupil had to queue a long time before they could obtained there food.

3. We therefore suggest that there should be two seperate sessions for lunch, the younger children can eat 20 minutes earlier then the oldest pupils.

4. This will also prevent the food to becoming cold and will enable the servers to work more careful, they are all in favour of this change.

5. We asked each pupil to complete a questionaire about the food, we used the information from them to produce the lists in Apendix 3

6. The tables what the pupils sit at are to crowded, so we recommend that only six pupils sit at each table, this will be possible if we have two sessions instead of one.

Using headings

(10 marks)

A classmate prepared to write a report on her school canteen. She jotted down these points:

amount of food	crowding	behaviour of pupils	servers
tables	pupil satisfaction	quality of food	cooks
cost of food	seating	cleanliness/hygiene	taste
(un)healthy food	hours/time	queues	waste

She showed you her notes and asked you for your opinion on arranging the points.

1   Suggest **five** main headings under which most or all of the points can be put.

_____

_____

_____

_____

_____

The pupils in Miss Wilson's class asked her if they could have a class picnic, so she asked them to plan the arrangements for a picnic. One pupil wrote about the following points but did not put them under any headings or in any clear order.

date	bus/car/train/coach	music/songs	weather – alternative indoors
times	food	drinks	parents – inform, come?
place	games	cost	activities

2   Suggest **five** main headings for a plan for the picnic.

_____

_____

_____

_____

_____

Unit 14

Conditional sentences

Key idea

A conditional sentence says that one thing depends on another. Conditional sentences usually contain the words **if** or **unless**. The "if" or "unless" part of the sentence is a special type of subordinate clause called a **conditional clause**.

conditional clause   main clause

If you tickle me, I will laugh.

What happens?

Complete these sentences in any sensible way. They are about habitual (usual) actions. *(10 marks – 2 marks for each correct sentence)*

1 If you leave ice out of a fridge, _____

2 If a player hits another player during a game of football, _____
_____

3 If people find that they have mice in their home, _____
_____

4 If it rains while the sun is shining, _____

5 If I'm very thirsty during the night, _____

What will probably happen?

Put in the right form of the verbs in brackets. The sentences are about things that may, can or probably will happen in future. *(5 marks – 0.5 mark for each correct answer)*

1 If a young child _____ (play) with matches at home, he or she _____ (start) a fire.

2 If it rains on Saturday, our Sports Day _____ (postpone). Then it _____ (hold) on 23 June.

3 If you _____ (eat) too much food, you _____ (put) on weight.

4 If you both stand on that table at the same time, it _____ (probably collapse) and you _____ (break) something.

5 If the rain doesn't stop soon, all this area _____ (flood) and we _____ (force) to leave our home.

Giving advice

We can use *If I were you ...* to give advice:

If I were you,	I wouldn't eat so much.
	I wouldn't bother to answer that email.
	I would be honest about it.

What advice can you give these friends or relatives? *(10 marks – 2 marks for each suitable answer)*

1   Dave says he always feels tired in the morning. He admits that he rarely goes to bed before 11 p.m. because his parents let him stay up to watch films.

   _____
   _____

2   You are visiting an aunt with your brother or sister. You have both been offered a cup of coffee, but you have declined the coffee politely. Your brother or sister is not sure whether or not to try drinking it and asks your advice.

   _____
   _____

3   A friend says she has several unwanted jigsaw puzzles at home. She is not sure whether to take them to a charity shop or just to throw them away. What do you advise?

   _____
   _____
   _____

4   A friend's family are going to spend a few days in Paris during the holidays. They can't decide whether to go by rail, ferry or air. Your friend mentioned this to you and said, "What would you do?"

   _____
   _____

5   A friend goes to a different school from yours. He tells you that he has noticed that two older boys are bullying younger pupils and making them pay money nearly every day. He is not sure what, if anything, he should do. He has asked for your advice. What do you suggest?

   _____
   _____

Other ways of showing a condition

We can also show a condition by making sentences like these:

You can go	provided that	you return before dark.
You can play with them	as long as	you're back by 700 p.m.
It's all right for you to go	on condition that	you are not late home again.

Use the information in each pair of sentences to make one sentence using one of the connectives in the second column above. You can change, omit or add words.
(5 marks)

1. You can go to Tom's house. You must be back here by 800 p.m.

2. You can borrow my bike. You must return it on Saturday.

3. Tom can stay with us for the weekend. His parents must agree.

4. I'll help you. Don't argue all the time.

5. We can have a picnic on Saturday. The weather must be fine then.

29

Narrative writing

Key idea

The purpose of a narrative text is to tell a story. Although individual stories can be very different, they all have some common structural and language features.

Zangram by C. J. Salter: extract 1

Read this extract from *Zangram*. Then answer the questions below. *(10 marks)*

1   The Logan family pulled wearily into a deserted car park not far from Stonehenge. Jack Logan, exhausted after driving for nine hours, said to his wife, "I need a rest."

"Good idea," his wife replied. "I told Sylvia we wouldn't be down 'til
5   noon."

Jack Logan glanced in the rear-view mirror. His children, Daniel and Claire, were sleeping soundly. So he settled down and was soon asleep himself.

Some time later, Claire stirred. The car seemed to be moving, but then
10   the movement stopped. She heard her dad snoring contentedly, and drifted back to sleep.

On board Spacecraft 462, the doors closed and a message flashed back to Zangram, far beyond Earth's solar system: "Mission completed. 20 specimens including four bipeds in a metal shell." The spaceship rose silently
15   from a field near Stonehenge and hurtled off into space. It carried with it the Logan family, their car, two inquisitive dogs, a deeply resentful cat and other specimens destined for examination and display in the Zangram national zoo.

1   In paragraph one, which word repeats the idea expressed by "wearily"? *(1 mark)*

_____

2   What were Mrs Logan's exact words when she spoke to Sylvia? *(1 mark)*

_____

3   What is missing before "Good idea" (line 4)? Why has it been left out? *(2 marks)*

_____

4   What adverb could we use instead of each of the following? (The adverb need not have the same meaning as the given word, but it must fit the situation.) *(4 marks)*

   a) soundly (line 7) _____   c) silently (line 14) _____

   b) contentedly (line 10) _____   d) deeply (line 16) _____

5   a) What does "inquisitive" tell us about the dogs? b) Why was the cat "resentful"? *(2 marks)*

   _____

Zangram: extract 2

Read this continuation of *Zangram*. Then answer the questions about it.
(10 marks)

> 1   When the Logan family woke up, they discovered they were in a huge glass dome. They were unaware, however, of the battery of tests and examinations that the Zangrams had carried out on them over a period of several days.
>
> 5   Outside the dome, a crowd of Zangrams watched the family through one-way glass. A notice outside the dome said, when translated into English, "On loan from Planet 264S/36 for 30 days". Of course, the Logans knew nothing of this. They believed that somehow they had been kidnapped.
>
>   "Well, at least we're alive," said Mrs Logan, trying to console her
> 10 children. "Sooner or later, we'll find out where we are and why we're here."
>
>   She was right. They found out the next day when the Zangrams had finally solved the riddle of Earth language and began to communicate with them.

1   What happened to the Logan family before they were put on display? *(2 marks)*

   _____

2   Why does the writer start a new paragraph in three places after the first paragraph? Give a reason why each of the three paragraphs has been started. *(3 marks)*

   _____

   _____

   _____

3   How does the phrase that begins the second paragraph link it to the first paragraph? *(2 marks)*

   _____

4 What does the pronoun "this" in line 8 refer to? *(1 mark)*

_____

5 How does the writer create a dramatic effect at the beginning of the last paragraph? *(2 marks)*

_____

Zangram: extract 3

Now read extract 3 and answer the questions about it. *(10 marks)*

1   When the Logans woke up in the car park at Stonehenge, they were puzzled to find their car turned round. They knew something odd had happened, but what? They drove on to Cornwall in some confusion. Their bewilderment deepened when they finally reached the home of Jack's brother and rang the
5   doorbell. Tony Logan opened the door and stared at them in a mixture of astonishment and horror.
   "Where have you been?" he said at last. "We were expecting you a month ago! We checked with your neighbours. We even informed the police because …"
10   "A month ago!" echoed Jack Logan. "We agreed July 10th and here we are."
   Tony stared at his brother, trying to decide whether he was joking or not. "But today is August 10th," he pointed out. "Anyway, come in. You're welcome at any time – even when you're officially 'missing, presumed dead'."
   Mrs Logan and the children went in. Jack went back to the car to unpack
15   the luggage. What he saw in the boot proved that something very strange had occurred.

1 What is similar about the ways in which extracts 1, 2 and 3 end? *(2 marks)*

_____

2 "We even informed the police because …" Why does the author insert …? *(1 mark)*

_____

3 Find five *different* uses of capital letters in the extract. *(5 marks)*

_____

_____

4 Write a sentence saying what Mr Logan found in the boot. *(2 marks)*

_____

Unit 17

Describing past events

Key idea

The purpose of writing a recount is to tell about a past event. Recount texts have some common structural and language features that help to identify them.

Time connectives

Read the account of a football match below. Put in ten different linking words or expressions. Choose from those below. *(10 marks)*

right up to the final whistle	shortly afterwards	at the start of the game
within the first ten minutes	ten minutes later	for the rest of the first half
during the half-time break	at half-time	ten minutes from the end
	immediately	

(1)_____ yesterday, Newtown were confidently expected to beat Oldtown by at least two goals. Newtown forced two corners (2)_____, but failed to score. Oldtown struck back but Jordan's shot was wide. (3)_____, Ken Teale put Newtown one up when he headed home a cross from Ojuro. Play was restricted to the centre of the field (4)_____ with Newtown slightly superior. (5)_____ the score remained Newtown 1 – Oldtown 0

Newtown manager, Joe Kellick, gave his men a pep-talk (6)_____. The players responded with raids on the Oldtown goal, during which Ken Teale scored his second goal. (7)_____ Oldtown veteran, Paul Cranston, scored for Oldtown. Stung by this unexpected goal, Newtown launched another series of attacks (8)_____ and were rewarded when Ojuro scored Newtown's third goal.

(9)_____ Tom Baxter shot wide for Oldtown. Defences dominated the game (10)_____.

Final score: Newtown 3 – Oldtown 1

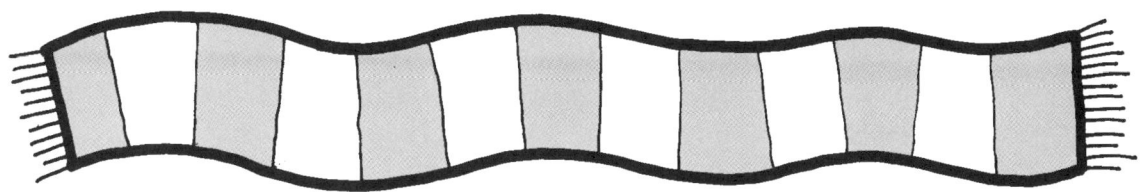

33

Exploring language

Read 'Hot water' and then answer the questions about it. *(20 marks)*

Hot water

1   Sue went to visit her grandfather, aged 90, in a remote rural district. Grandad cooked a very tasty lunch. However, when Sue put the plates and cutlery on the table, she noticed some tiny brown specks on her plate. She studied the plate thoughtfully for a few moments.

5   "Grandad," she asked hesitantly. "Are you … Are these plates clean?"

"Of course they are," Grandad replied quickly. "They're as clean as hot water can get them. That's for sure. Enjoy your meal and don't worry about the plates."

In the evening, Sue helped Grandad to prepare supper. She was hungry and
10 was just about to put the food on the plates when she saw a thin piece of something on one of the plates. It looked like scrambled egg.

"Grandad," she said firmly. "Are you absolutely sure these plates are clean?"

"No doubt about it," Grandad said with a smile. "They're as clean as hot
15 water can make them. I can guarantee that."

A few minutes later, a neighbour approached Grandad's house. Immediately his dog started to bark furiously. Grandad shouted angrily at the dog, "Cut that out, Hotwater! No more barking! Go and lay down! It's only Jim. You know him."

20 "I call her 'Hotwater'," Grandad explained to Sue, "because she always gets me into trouble."

"Ugh!" Sue thought. "I wonder if … I think I've been had."

"Grandad," she said quietly, "I'll wash the dishes tonight."

1   a) Underline any ten adjectives in the passage. *(5 marks)*

   b) Choose six of the adjectives and give words opposite in meaning to them. *(3 marks)*

   _____   _____

   _____   _____

   _____   _____

2   Choose three verbs used in the past tense in the passage. Write them down and then write the present and future tenses of each. *(3 marks)*

   _____

   _____

   _____

3   At the end of the third sentence, what one word can we insert after "plate" to turn the following sentence into a subordinate clause?_____ *(1 mark)*

4   Suggest a reason why Sue was hesitant when she first asked Grandad if the plates were clean? *(1 mark)*

   _____

5   Complete the sentence. *(1 mark)*

   "In line 6, the writer uses 'as … as' to_____

6   a) Write down any six adverbs in the passage. *(3 marks)*

   _____   _____

   _____   _____

   _____   _____

   b) Choose any four of the adverbs and write down words opposite in meaning to them. *(2 marks)*

7   What did Sue mean when she said, "I think I've been had"? *(1 mark)*

   _____

35

Unit 18 Giving instructions

Key idea

Instructions, directions and descriptions of procedures all have to be written clearly and concisely so they are easy to follow. Features such as sequenced and numbered steps, imperative verbs and sequencing connectives are common to this type of writing.

Checklist

Paul wrote the following checklist for maintaining his bike. Read it and then answer the questions about it. *(15 marks)*

> Checklist for maintaining bicycles
> 1. Check <u>brake</u> cables. Do brake blocks make good contact with rims of wheels?
> 2. Is <u>bell</u> fastened firmly? Does it work properly?
> 3. Check if front and rear <u>lights</u>. Replace battry or check dynamo if necessary.
> 4. <u>Chain</u> – tighten and see if any oil is needed.
> 5. <u>Saddle</u> – make sure it is at the right height and comfortable.
> 6. <u>Carrier</u> – check that nuts holding carrier are not lose. Tighten?
> 7. Check nuts holding <u>wheels</u> in place. Tighten or replace if necessary.
> 8. Check air in <u>tyres</u>; check for slow punctures.
> 9. Grease or oil any points that need lubricating, e.g. wheel <u>axils</u>.
> 10. Check that <u>tyre valves</u> are working properly.
> 11. Buy <u>padlock</u> with at least two keys. Get extra keys cut?

1. In step 2, are "firmly" and "properly" adjectives or adverbs?
   _____ *(2 marks)*

2. In step 3, what words are missing from the first sentence?
   _____ *(2 marks)*

3. How could Paul do step 5? _____ *(2 marks)*

4. Find four misspelt words and correct them. *(4 marks)*
   _____   _____

   _____   _____

5. Rewrite step 2 as a single statement with an imperative verb. *(2 marks)*
   _____

6 Which two steps could you combine so that there are only ten steps? *(2 marks)*

_____

7 What is the purpose of step 11? *(1 mark)*

_____

Defrosting a freezer

Rewrite Gran's instructions for how to defrost a freezer. Set them out in the right order using no more than ten steps. Leave out points that are not necessary.
(15 marks)

> Well, of course, you have to make sure that you don't make a mess in the kitchen. We don't want any water left on the floor to make the place slippery. That's how Grandad broke a leg a few years ago. Get a few old towels (there are plenty at the bottom of the airing-cupboard) and take them to the freezer. Oh, yes, you'll need a pail or a saucepan to put the water in. Put one of the towels on the floor in front of the freezer to catch the drips. Now, where was I? Ah, yes, empty the freezer. There are only a couple of packets in it now. Stick them in the fridge. Turn off the electricity. Open the freezer wide. Put a couple of towels inside to soak up the water. If you're in a hurry, put a bowl of hot water on a shelf in the freezer. It will help to thaw out the ice. You can poke any pieces of ice free if you like but it's not necessary.
>
> Leave the freezer door open and just be patient. When the ice has all gone, wring out the towels. Clean and dry the freezer. Get rid of any water. Then put the packets back in the freezer and turn it on. Easy!

Unit 19: Writing reports

Key idea

Report texts present information on a subject. They describe things as they are. They often feature present-tense verbs, descriptive adjectives and adverbs, and headings and subheadings.

The breakfast report

(10 marks)

1. "Write a report about breakfast in your family," said the teacher to Paul's class. If you were in the class, how would you arrange your ideas? Think of headings for three paragraphs. *(3 marks)*

   _____

   _____

   _____

Breakfast by Paul

We have three different kinds of breakfast, classified according to how it is eaten.

My favourite is a "sitting-down" breakfast. It is a leisurely event on Saturday and Sunday because I do not have to get up early. It includes cereal, fried eggs, beans, mushrooms, toast and jam and a big glass of orange juice.

A "standing-up" breakfast involves a drink, toast and a piece of fruit. I usually have this on school days because I have less time.

When I forget to set the alarm and am late for school, I have to have an "on-the-move" breakfast. I shoot out of the house, buy a chocolate bar and eat it before the bell rings.

---

2. Write paragraph headings for Paul's report above. *(3 marks)*

   _____

   _____

   _____

3. What part of speech is each of these words as it is used in Paul's report? *(4 marks)*
   a) classified _____   b) leisurely _____
   c) usually _____   d) shoot _____

The rodent report

This is part of a report on squirrels, written by Sally, age 11 Read it and then answer the questions about it. *(10 marks)*

> **Grey squirrels**
>
> **Where they came from**
>
> Grey squirrels were brought to Britain from America many years ago and kept in zoos. Some excaped and spread to both rural and urban areas. They have now driven red squirrels away.
>
> _____
>
> They prefer to eat seeds, berries and especially nuts, so they can often be found near oak, beech and other nut trees. However, they also eat birds' eggs and baby birds. Therefore, the presents of squirrels often leads to the absence of birds since they cannot nest safely.
>
> **How they behave**
>
> Grey squirrels are active during the day and do not hibernate in winter. They are naturaly shy, but not when it comes to food. In some towns, squirrels in parks are so tame that they will take peanuts, if offered, from people's hands.
>
> **The problems they cause**
>
> Grey squirrels (in fact, all kinds of squirrels) can be pests. They raid berries and other fruit from bushes and trees in poeple's gardens. They also gnaw and eat bark, which leads to the death of trees.

1. a) Circle the passive verb in the first paragraph. *(1 mark)*
   b) Why is the verb not active? *(1 mark)* _____

2. Fill in the missing subheading for the second paragraph. *(2 marks)*

3. Draw a box around each of the connectives in the second paragraph. (Do not include "and".) *(2 marks)*

4. Find the four misspelled words in the report. Draw a line through each one and write the correctly spelled word above. *(2 marks)*

5. In the last sentence of the third paragraph, underline the main clause once and the subordinate clause twice. *(2 marks)*

Write a worm report

(10 marks)

Here are some notes about worms.
1 Think of four different headings under which you could group the notes.
2 Then write a four-paragraph report using the notes.

- Do not like light
- Eat dead leaves and soil
- Has complete digestive system
- Help plants to grow
- Live underground
- Long, soft bodies with head and tail end
- Make tunnels to move about
- No bones, eyes, legs
- Soil leaves body making worm "casts"
- Useful creatures – tunnels bring air to soil
- Use muscles and hairs on skin to move
- Take nutrients from soil as it passes through body

WORMS

Paragraph 1 heading:_____

Paragraph 2 heading:_____

Paragraph 3 heading:_____

Paragraph 4 heading:_____

unit 20 Persuasive writing

Key idea

Persuasive writing aims to influence the reader towards a particular opinion. It often uses emotional words, figurative devices and imperative verbs.

Email scam

Mrs Stone received this email, which is full of mistakes. Fortunately, she knew it was not from her bank at all, but an attempt by someone to find out her details illegally. Read it and answer the questions. *(10 marks)*

> Subject: Confirm your details to avoid immediate cancellation to your account.
>
> Yesterday the bank have a failure of its software this resulted in a lost of customer data. To help you to avoid from fraud, kindly connect with the link below to confirm your account registration data, this is obligatory to protect your account.
>
> Please do not answer to this message. Fill in the form "Confirmation of Acount Details".

1 Which words in the "subject" are meant to frighten the receiver? *(1 mark)*

2 Find an incorrect verb tense. Explain why it is wrong and correct it. *(2 marks)*

3 Find two places where punctuation is wrong or missing. Correct them. *(2 marks)*

4 Find and correct four expressions in which prepositions are used wrongly. *(2 marks)*

5 Find and correct two spelling mistakes. *(2 marks)*

6 Why does the sender of the email put in the sentence, "This is obligatory to protect your account"? *(1 mark)*

41

**The mighty T-watch is here:
hep, handy, helpful!**

It's COOL and it could be yours!

On one side, it's a watch.
No need to look at it.

Press the button and it tells you the time. Now that's really something – but there's more!

On the other side? A nifty recorder. Up to 10 minutes talktime. No need to take notes.

**Move up to the in-crowd!
ORDER NOW
before they're all snapped up.**

"I love it!" says pop star Kati Lane.

Football legend, Mike O'Shea:
"I wouldn't be without mine!"

An advertisement

Read the advertisement above and then answer these questions. *(10 marks)*

1   Which slang words in the advertisment mean "up-to-date, fashionable"? *(1 mark)*

2   What figurative device is used in the second line? *(1 mark)*

3   Why is "COOL" put in capital letters? *(1 mark)*

4   "On the other side? A nifty recorder." Explain why the writer doesn't use complete sentences. *(2 marks)*

5   Why does the advertiser use the word "nifty" instead of "clever"? *(1 mark)*

6   Explain the purpose of the pictures. *(2 marks)*

7   Give one example each of two different verb forms used in the advertisement. *(1 mark)*

8   In the first draft of this advertisement, the advertiser wrote : "Keep up with the in-crowd". Why did she change this to "Move up to the in-crowd"? *(1 mark)*

Getting involved

Miss Benson's class wrote to their local council following three traffic accidents near their school. Read their first draft below and then answer the questions.
(10 marks)

> In the passed six months, there have been three horrific traffic acidents near our school, each time somebody was knocked down by a speeding motorist. We beg the Council to do something to make Bridge Street safer.
>
> We would like to recommend four crucial measures. First of all, we hope the Council can put some speed bumps in the road to slow down traffic. Secondly, we need a pedestran crossing outside our school. Thirdly, it would be a good idea to errect warning sines at each end of Bridge Street, finally, we think that cars should not be aloud to park outside our school for longer than 15 minutes during 8–9 a.m. and 3–4 p.m. on school days.

1. Why do the children mention accidents in their letter? *(1 mark)*
   _____

2. Give two examples of powerful, emotive words in the letter. Why do the children use them? *(2 marks)*
   _____   _____
   _____

3. Find and correct six spelling mistakes in the draft letter. *(3 marks)*
   _____   _____   _____
   _____   _____   _____

4. Find two places where a comma should be replaced by a full stop. *(1 mark)*
   _____   _____

5. Find a passive verb in the first paragraph. *(1 mark)*
   _____

6. List the sequencing connectives used in the second paragraph. *(1 mark)*
   _____

7. How might the children revise the layout of the second paragraph so that their suggestions are clearer? *(1 mark)*
   _____

Unit 21 Writing discussion texts

Key idea

Discussion texts give a balanced presentation of all the various positions that are held about an issue or topic – for example, both sides of an argument.

Television: points of view

"Does television do more harm than good?" Read the first draft of what one pupil wrote and then answer the questions about it. *(10 marks)*

1 Most television shows have a bad influence to viewers, especially young ones. They use swear words and bad language most of the time. Violence is common in "soaps" and are regarded as a model or example to teenagers.

On the other hand, documentries are both educational and intresting. There is always
5 something new for viewers to learn as long as they can stay awake. Oddly enough, the cartoons are usually OK. They are always amusing without setting a bad example. Sports programmes are also worth watching and do not cause no harm or offence.

Maybe the only fair answer to the question is that the affect of TV depends upon the individual. If you have firm principals, you can always chose wisely. I hope that television
10 channels will clean up their act, but I won't hold my breathe waiting for that to happen.

1 What more accurate word should the writer use instead of "most" in lines 1 and 2? *(1 mark)*

2 In lines 1 and 3, replace "to" with correct prepositions. *(2 marks)*

3 Explain and correct the error of agreement in the third sentence. *(1 mark)*

4 Explain and correct the error in the last sentence of the second paragraph. *(1 mark)*

5 Correct six spelling mistakes in the last two paragraphs. *(3 marks)*

6 Is the writer's discussion well-balanced? Explain your answer. *(2 marks)*

Maths – or no maths?

"Should children be allowed to decide whether they want to study maths or not?" Read the first draft of what one pupil wrote and then answer the questions about it. *(10 marks)*

1 Some people say that we do not need maths in our daily lifes because calculaters and computers can give us all the answers. I don't agree to that because sometimes if we don't know any maths it is easy for crooks to cheat us. Also we need maths whenever we buy or sell anything and maybe we have no calculator available.

5 On the other hand, it is true that algebra and geometry can be too difficult to some children and they become confused and fed up. Then they may even hate the subject and start to behave badly at school. Perhaps the right thing to do is to make basic maths compulsery up to, say, the age of 14 and to make it optional after that. If somebody is no good at maths (even when he or she tries very hard), it is a waist of time to force the

10 person to continue to study the subject.

1 Find and correct four spelling errors: two in each paragraph *(2 marks)*

2 Correct the mistakes in the use of prepositions in lines 2 and 5 *(1 mark)*

3 What more formal words could the writer use instead of "crooks" (line 3) and "fed up" (line 6)? *(1 mark)*

4 How many points for each side of the argument does the writer give? What are they? *(4 marks)*

5 Do you agree with the writer's conclusion? Give reasons for your answer. *(2 marks)*

45

Should it be a crime to kill any wild animal?

(10 marks)

Put a suitable word in each blank space. *(7 marks – 0.5 mark for each correct answer)*

I am in favour of protecting wild animals, but there (1)_____ two main reasons (2)_____ I do not think it (3)_____ be a crime to kill any wild animal. Firstly, sometimes it is (4)_____ to kill wild animals such as mice, rats and rabbits. (5)_____ we do not kill some of them, they will increase (6)_____ cause serious problems. A (7)_____ reason is that sometimes wild animals, such (8)_____ boars, foxes, badgers and deer, increase and (9)_____ a threat to farmers. Then it is necessary to kill some of (10)_____.

We must also remember (11)_____ some farmers keep cattle, sheep, deer, goats and (12)_____ animals for their milk or meat. Are these wild animals? If somebody kills a wild pony on Dartmoor (13)_____ that a crime? As I said earlier, I think some wild animals should be protected, but making it a crime to kill one is not the (14)_____ way of doing it.

- Do you think it should be a crime to kill wild animals? Give two reasons for your answer. *(3 marks)*

_____
_____
_____
_____
_____

Unit 22

Investigating English expressions

Key idea

Investigating language is the best way to find out how it works.

American English

(16 marks)

Americans speak English, but many of their words differ from British English. Do you know what they're talking about? Put the right British word by each American word below. *(8 marks – 0.5 mark for each correct answer)*

| taxi   pavement   sweets   dummy (for a baby)   nappy   trousers |
| autumn   boot (of a car)   lorry   curtains   petrol   sweet biscuits |
| lift   handbag   queue   tap (for water) |

1 cab _____

2 line _____

3 fall _____

4 truck _____

5 diaper _____

6 purse _____

7 candy _____

8 pants _____

9 trunk (of a car) _____

10 gas(oline) _____

11 pacifier _____

12 cookies _____

13 faucet _____

14 sidewalk _____

15 drapes _____

16 elevator _____

Now find out for yourself the British words for these American words. *(8 marks)*

17 drugstore _____

18 closet _____

19 stove _____

20 hood (of a car) _____

21 vacation _____

22 garbage _____

23 movies _____

24 buck (money) _____

Investigating idioms

Put the right idiom on each line below. *(14 marks)*

- a Tartar
- eyewash
- a close shave
- a mouthpiece
- a square peg in a round hole
- a rough diamond
- a pig in a poke
- a fool's paradise
- a blank cheque
- a fly in the ointment
- a red herring
- a hornets' nest
- soft soap
- a white lie

1. A _____ is an untrue statement which is made for good reasons, for example to protect an innocent person.

2. _____ is something (usually a statement) meant to deceive people or hide something wrong.

3. _____ is a person who is very difficult to deal with even if you have some advantage over them. Many years ago, if you captured this person in a battle, he would prove a troublesome prisoner.

4. _____ is something which is meant to deceive you, perhaps by making you look in the wrong direction when trying to solve a problem.

5. _____ is permission to do as you like, for example to spend as much money as you like because the cheque has been signed but no amount has been put in.

6. If you spend a lot of time dreaming about winning a lottery, you may live in _____, thinking about something nice which will never happen.

7. If you buy _____, you buy something (such as a pig tied up in a sack) before you have had a chance to inspect it.

8. _____ is flattery.

9. _____ is somebody who appears tough or lacking in manners, but is really very kind and generous.

10. If a person is in a job that does not suit him or her, we may say that the person is _____.

11. _____ is an obstacle to a plan.

12. Sometimes we call a narrow escape _____.

13. _____ is somebody who speaks on behalf of another person or organisation, often to give excuses or reasons for an action.

14. _____ is a source of possible trouble because if you interfere you may create a worse situation.

Key Grammar is a brand new resource, specifically planned to cover all the key grammar objectives in self-contained units of work. The pupil books feature:

- clear, progressive units covering all key learning objectives
- plenty of practice and consolidation work
- opportunities to challenge and extend children's learning
- a clear mark scheme
- exercises in an appropriate context, with engaging illustrations

The workbooks provide activities for additional practice, differentiation, and homework. The important language skills coverage in **Key Grammar** is complemented by two associated series: **Key Comprehension** and **Key Spelling** – up-to-date and engaging resources which reinforce key teaching points and enable children to practise, consolidate and extend their learning. For further information about **Key Comprehension** and **Key Spelling** call our Customer Services Department on **(+44) (0)1865 888000.**

ISBN 978-0-602206-85-7

Author: Alan Etherton

Ginn is an imprint of Pearson education Limited, a company incorporated in England and Wales, having its registered office at Edinburgh Gate, Harlow, Essex, CM20 2JE.
Registered company number: 872828

www.ginn.co.uk
Help and support for teachers plus the widest range of education solutions

© Harcourt Education Limited 2005

This book is copyright and reproduction of the whole or part without the publishers' written permission is prohibited.

Key Grammar Workbook 4
ISBN: 978 0602 20685 7
Level 4 Easy Order Pack: 978 0602 20651 2
Level 4 Workbook 6 Pack: 978 0602 20648 2

First published 2005

16
13

Cover illustration by Pet Gotohda
Cover design by Tom Cole
Designed by Nicki Wise, Te Marama Design
Illustrations by David Semple, Gary Swift, Andrew Painter

Printed and bound in China (GCC/13)

Grammar Workbook 4

Contents

Unit 1	Word classes	page 2
Unit 2	Using standard English	page 4
Unit 3	Active and passive verbs 1	page 6
Unit 4	Connectives	page 8
Unit 5	Forming complex sentences 1	page 10
Unit 6	Punctuation	page 12
Unit 8	Active and passive verbs 2	page 14
Unit 9	Official language	page 16
Unit 10	Forming complex sentences 2	page 18
Unit 11	Making notes	page 20
Unit 12	Writing a summary	page 22
Unit 13	Editing	page 24
Unit 14	Conditional sentences	page 27
Unit 16	Narrative writing	page 30
Unit 17	Describing past events	page 33
Unit 18	Giving instructions	page 36
Unit 19	Writing reports	page 38
Unit 20	Persuasive writing	page 41
Unit 21	Writing discussion texts	page 44
Unit 22	Investigating English expressions	page 47

Unit 1 Word classes

🔑 Key idea

Words are categorised in classes according to the jobs they do in a sentence: noun, pronoun, verb, adjective, adverb, preposition, conjunction and interjection. Words can belong to more than one class.

Work it out

Give one-word answers. *(10 marks)*

1 Which proper noun is the name of the Italian capital? _____
2 Which adjective is the opposite of "wise"? _____
3 Which collective noun means "a lot of (birds flying) together"? _____
4 Which verb means "to tremble with cold or fear"? _____
5 Which pronoun is the opposite of "no one"? _____
6 Which proper noun is the name of the shortest month of the year? _____
7 Which adverb is the opposite of "rarely"? _____
8 What is the second part of the conjunction "not only…"? _____
9 What adverb can we form from "skill"? _____
10 Which verb means to "make longer"? _____

Which word?

Ring or underline the right word in the brackets. *(10 marks)*

1 It was dark, so we couldn't see (nothing, anything) clearly.
2 Would you mind (to wait, waiting) a few minutes?
3 There (are, is) more than one way of solving this problem.
4 Where (are, is) the rest of the players?
5 The change in the plan will not have a great deal of (affect, effect) on us.
6 Don't be so (impatience, impatient), John!
7 Between you and (I, me), I think Margaret is quite right to be suspicious.
8 This photo is different (than, from) that one.
9 We watched the marathon, but we did not (took, take) part in it.
10 Your new bike is much better than (Paul's, Pauls').

Classify it

Read this passage from *Nicholas Nickleby* by Charles Dickens. Place each of the underlined words under the correct heading in the grid below. *(10 marks – 0.5 mark for each correctly placed word)*

Dotheboy's Hall <u>was</u> not a hall at all, <u>but</u> a bare and dirty room with a <u>couple</u> of windows, in which most of the glass was broken. There were a few old <u>rickety</u> desks, <u>cut</u> and notched, and inked and damaged, in <u>every</u> possible way; a detached desk for <u>Squeers</u>; and another <u>for</u> his assistant. The ceiling was supported, like <u>that</u> of a barn, by cross beams and rafters; and the walls were so stained that it was impossible to tell <u>whether</u> they had ever been painted or whitewashed.

But the pupils! How his last hopes <u>faded</u> as <u>he</u> looked <u>around</u>! Pale and haggard faces of old men, boys of stunted growth, and others whose long thin legs would <u>hardly</u> carry their <u>stooping</u> bodies, all <u>crowded</u> together; there were the bleary eye, the hare-lip, the crooked foot, and every problem arising from <u>cruelty</u> and neglect. There were little faces which should have been handsome, darkened with the scowl of suffering; there were vicious-faced boys, brooding like prisoners in jail; <u>and</u> there were children <u>who</u> were weeping <u>with</u> loneliness…

nouns	
pronouns	
verbs	
adjectives	
adverbs	
prepositions	
conjunctions	

Unit 2 Using standard English

Key idea

We can use non-standard English in speech, but we must use standard English in formal written work.

Does it agree?

Underline the subject each time. (It may be a single word or a group of words.) Then circle the right word in the brackets so that the verb agrees with its subject.
(14 marks)

1 How much of the information in newspaper reports or radio and television news reports (are, is) completely accurate?

2 According to a report on television, a reward of several thousand pounds (has, have) been offered for information leading to the arrest of the robbers.

3 The driver of the bus – together with two of the passengers – (was, were) slightly injured in the accident.

4 (Is, Are) there any mud on your shoes?

5 The number of flights from London to Spain (have, has) risen in recent years because more people like to spend a holiday on the Spanish coast.

6 There (is, are) a number of reasons why people prefer to spend their holiday abroad. The main attraction is the better climate overseas.

7 What a nuisance! All the traffic (has, have) stopped. There must have been an accident somewhere ahead of us.

8 Before the play started, a member of the cast peeped through the curtains and said, "Oh, good! The audience (is, are) a really big one tonight. There are no empty seats."

9 Everybody in our class (want, wants) to join in the picnic, don't they?

10 How long (has, have) all this rubbish been lying here?

11 As a result of a change in the law, the poor (is, are) likely to be better off.

12 A good standard of numeracy (is, are) necessary in many jobs.

13 At least a third of those players (is, are) from foreign countries.

14 The majority of the pupils in our class (does, do) not come to school in a car.

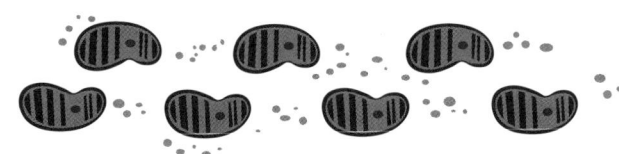

Choose the right word

Ring or underline the right words in the brackets. *(8 marks)*

1. This shop doesn't sell cosmetics (or, nor) health foods.
2. My sister doesn't like garlic and (so, nor) do I.
3. Sometimes people are not sure where to keep their money. If they hide (them, it) at home, there is always a risk of burglary.
4. The manager told his staff that he hadn't (no, any) intention of resigning.
5. John did not feel very well at the start of the cross-country race, and he felt much (worse, worser) at the end.
6. After the show, my friend and (me, I) bought some chips and ate (it, them) on the way home.
7. We need somebody to check all the electrical (equipment, equipments) before we turn on the computer and heating.
8. Our visit to Scandinavia (maybe, may be) described as a tour rather than a holiday.

Make it formal

Write more formal expressions that we can use instead of the italic words. *(8 marks)*

1. That's a *lousy* idea. _____
2. There's a rumour that their business is *on the rocks*. _____
3. All the *kids* in my class agree with me. _____
4. I haven't got *nothing* special to tell you. _____
5. The man said he didn't know *no one* with that name. _____
6. The fact that he is guilty *sticks out like a sore thumb*. _____
7. This hairstyle is gradually *catching on*. _____
8. *How come* you're not at school today? _____

Unit 3 Active and passive verbs 1

🔑 Key idea

Verbs can be in the **active** or **passive** voice.

A dangerous job

Write in the *passive* Simple Present form of the verbs in brackets. *(12 marks)*

In Malaysia, rubber (1)_____ (grow) on many estates. At dawn, rubber-tappers start work. Many of them are women and they know that their work can be dangerous. Sometimes tappers (2)_____ (attack) by a tiger. When they bend down to tap a tree, they (3)_____ (sometimes mistake) for a wild animal and attacked by a hungry tiger.

Tappers start work before the sun rises. First, a cut (4)_____ (make) in a mature tree. A tin or half a coconut shell (5)_____ (fasten) to the tree. It (6)_____ (use) to collect latex from the cut. The tapper cuts many trees. Then he or she returns to the first tree. Latex in the tin (7)_____ (empty) into a pail which (8)_____ (take) to the small "factory" on the estate. Chemicals (9)_____ (add) to the latex and mixed in well. Later on, the latex (10)_____ (squeeze) into sheets which (11)_____ (hang) in a smoke-filled hut. Finally, the sheets of rubber (12)_____ (tie) up in bales, ready for export to other countries.

A gas leak

Put in the *passive* form of the verbs in brackets. Use *has/have been + a past participle* each time. *(10 marks)*

One evening Mrs Wilson (Mrs W) was on her way home from work. She got off a bus and started to walk the 200 metres to her home. As she walked round a corner, she was surprised to see a crowd of people outside a wrecked house. There were fire-engines and police cars there too. Mrs Wilson's friend, Mrs Johnson (Mrs J), was in the crowd.

Mrs W: What's the matter? What's happened?

Mrs J: There was a gas leak. That house (1)_____ (wreck) completely.

Mrs W: (2)_____ anybody _____(injure)?

Mrs J: Yes, two people (3)_____ (hurt). They (4)_____ (take) to hospital already.

Mrs W: What are the fire-engines doing here?

Mrs J: There was a small fire but it (5)_____ (bring) under control. The gas company (6)_____ (inform), so men are coming to repair the pipe. A lot of debris (7)_____ (hurl) across the road, so the windows in those houses (8)_____ (break). The people in those houses (9)_____ (evacuate). There were some elderly people in that old folks' home over there. They (10) _____ (move) to another home temporarily.

Mrs W: Is there anything we can do to help?

Mrs J: No, I don't think so.

In trouble

Put in the *passive* future form of the verbs in brackets. Use *will be* + *a past participle*. *(8 marks)*

Paul's friend, Mike, was sent off during a football match for hitting an opponent. Now Paul is asking his dad, a referee, what will happen to Mike.

Paul: Will Mike get into trouble?

Dad: Yes, I'm afraid he will. I'm sure he (1)_____ (charge) with hitting an opponent. Then he (2)_____ (ask) to attend a hearing before the Disciplinary Committee. He (3)_____ (tell) what he is charged with.

Paul: What will happen after that?

Dad: He (4)_____ (give) a chance to listen to the referee's report and ask any questions. Then he (5)_____ (invite) to make his statement and admit the charge or try to deny it.

Paul: I don't think he will deny it because everybody saw what happened. What will the Committee do?

Dad: Well, Mike (6)_____ (inform) of the decision in writing. It is probable that he (7)_____ (ban) for a few months. If he has a bad record, he (8)_____ (fine) as well, I should think.

Unit 4 Connectives

Key idea

Connectives are words and phrases that are used to link different parts of a text. They can join words, phrases, clauses, sentences and paragraphs.

Types of connectives

Underline the connectives in the sentences below. Then put them under the correct heading in the grid. *(10 marks)*

1. Paul decided to buy the bicycle although it was expensive.
2. We can go out when the rain stops.
3. Mary stuck a stamp on the envelope and then she posted the invitation.
4. Following my operation, I developed an infection in the wound.
5. We can go for a picnic on Saturday if the weather is good.
6. Mike can't go out to play now because he hasn't finished his homework yet.
7. You can go to London by train or you can travel on the express bus.
8. Our new house is bigger than our old one. Moreover, it has a large garden.
9. Most people like Susan, but I think she is rather conceited.
10. Despite having a terrible cold, the soprano performed her solo.

Addition	Time	Cause and effect	Opposition

Connective starters

Complete each sentence in a suitable way to show that you understand the connective. *(10 marks)*

1 We'll have to wait here until _____
2 If you eat too much, _____
3 We couldn't move the wardrobe because _____
4 Although it snowed last night, _____
5 In spite of the cold weather, _____
6 Kate is very fond of animals, so _____
7 Choose your sweets and then _____
8 I forgot to set the alarm. As a result, _____
9 The game started on time despite _____
10 I often eat fish. However, _____

Choosing connectives

Ring or underline the right word in the brackets. *(10 marks)*

1 We can go there by taxi. (Alternately, Alternatively) we can take the bus.

2 (Despite, In spite) the discount, Mrs Lee decided not to buy the car.

3 We had to leave our house when a pipe burst. Now we're waiting for the workmen to complete the repairs. In the (while, meantime), we're staying with my grandparents.

4 The team has succeeded because the owner of the club is a billionaire. (Nevertheless, Furthermore) it has one of the best managers in Europe.

5 Crocodiles have no predators to attack them. (Consequently, Subsequently) they manage to live for many years.

6 Trees can spread their seeds in many ways. (Meanwhile, For example,) sycamore seeds have "wings" to help them fly away from the parent tree.

7 We don't agree with Paul's plan. On the (other hand, contrary), we think it could be disastrous for the club.

8 His plan contains several faults. (Nevertheless, Similarly) it contains some good points.

9 You ought to buy yourself a watch (instead of, in spite of) borrowing mine.

10 Most shops have security cameras (providing, so that) they can catch thieves.

unit 5 Forming complex sentences 1

🔑 Key idea

Complex sentences are made up of more than one clause.
The clauses can be joined in different ways.

Completing sentences

**Complete these sentences in any sensible way.
Draw a ring round the connecting words.** *(10 marks)*

1 A library is a place where _____

2 There was a hidden cottage where_____

3 Don't forget to turn the lights off when _____

4 People go to a dentist when _____

5 Plants will usually grow well if _____

6 Traffic police may stop a motorist if _____

7 Mary had the flu last week, so _____

8 Paul could not hear what people were saying on television, so _____
_____

9 You can go to your friend's house now, provided that _____
_____

10 You can borrow my bike if you like, provided that _____
_____

What and where?

Complete each sentence by saying *what* people are doing and *where* they are doing it. Start with a present participle (an –ing word) *(10 marks)*

Example: We watched some men **repairing** a pipe in the road near our home.

1 Ashra heard two women _____

2 When I came out of my house, I noticed a man _____
_____

3 When we reached the beach, we saw some fishermen _____
_____

10

4   Before we entered the park, we stopped to watch some boys _____

5   When Sue looked out of the window, she saw a blackbird _____

6   Last night on television we watched some girls _____

7   After a few minutes, the fox came to a field and was happy to see some lambs _____

8   Mr Evans woke up during the night when he heard somebody _____

9   When our bus passed Mary's house, we saw her father _____

10 The lifeguard ran down the beach when he heard somebody _____

Punctuating complex sentences

Put in the missing commas. *(10 marks)*

1   Yesterday in broad daylight the police caught two men trying to rob a bank.

2   The frightened rabbit stayed absolutely still hoping that the fox had not seen it.

3   My father the manager of the store starts work before 8 a.m.

4   Last night the temperature in most Welsh towns was above freezing-point. In Aberystwyth however it was minus four degrees.

5   Did you enjoy yourself at the party last Saturday Kate?

6   Although the concert lasted for over two hours the audience was captivated by the soloist who was only ten.

7   Not having seen her cousin for several years Sue was surprised to see how tall he was.

8   Birmingham is a very large city. In fact it is one of the largest in the United Kingdom.

9   When the phone rang Peter hurried to answer it hoping that it was his friend.

10 Leaping over the wall the frightened animal disappeared into the woods.

Unit 6 Punctuation

Key idea

Adding clauses increases the complexity of sentences, so more punctuation is required.

Using commas

Put in commas where necessary. The sentences show various different uses of commas. *(10 marks)*

1 The home of the Duke of Devonshire has 173 rooms and houses more than 60 types of clocks.

2 Paul go and find Mary please.

3 Worms are probably the most common bait for fish. If you expect to catch fish therefore you must be prepared to handle worms.

4 'Ugh! I'm not going to touch a worm' Katie said.

5 One of our neighbours Mrs Collins is a very experienced nurse.

6 Even if I were a billionaire I would not want to live alone in a huge isolated house.

7 Very few people read poetry books in their leisure time. Many modern pop songs however contain their own type of poetry and are very popular.

8 When tadpoles get older their tails get shorter their legs get longer and they gradually develop into very small frogs.

9 Pauline Taylor whose father is a maths teacher is always top of the class in maths not surprisingly.

10 If you're ready it's time for us to leave for the airport Grandad.

Using speech marks

Each of these unpunctuated sentences contains direct speech. Rewrite them, putting in the speech marks and other punctuation marks and capital letters that are necessary. *(10 marks)*

1 My friend said to me would you mind checking this letter for me please

2 I told her you've left an r out of preferred

3   Miss Lee told me you should have written chose and not choose

4   I heard Paul shout out wait for me Mike so we waited for him

5   If you've finished your homework my mother said you can watch the film on TV

6   when the performance ended the audience rose to their feet and shouted bravo

7   clamouring up the treacherous rocks the mountain rescuer cried hold on

8   can i follow you asked grace i dont know the way besides its dark

9   the wizard whose wand was misbehaving shook his finger and said abracadabra

10 louise rubbed her eyes yawned and mumbled whats the matter

More punctuation practice

Put in any necessary punctuation marks and capital letters. *(10 marks)*

1   its the end of march tomorrow remember to put your clocks on an hour

2   remember what people say in america spring forward fall back

3   in sentence 2 the word fall means autumn

4   there are 24 children in our class 14 boys and 10 girls

5   i think that jacket is a real bargain don't you mary

6   that was my first visit to a zoo I thought it was very interesting

7   come in sit down would you like a soft drink

8   some girls like to play netball or rounders others prefer hockey

9   the speaker promised the people many things more jobs higher pay longer holidays and lower taxes

10 don't forget the saying nothing ventured nothing gained

Unit 8

Active and passive verbs 2

Key idea

Verbs can be in the **active** or **passive** voice.

Look to the future

Read the two passages. Write in the *passive* future form of the verbs in brackets.
(10 marks)

A. Tomorrow part of the motorway (1)_____ (close) for urgent resurfacing. The work (2)_____ (complete) by 4 p.m., when the road (3)_____ (reopen) to traffic. While the road is closed, traffic (4)_____(divert). Notices (5)_____ (put) up to show motorists the route to follow.

B. Miss Harris told her class, "Our Sports Day will be on next Friday. It (6)_____ (hold) on the school field, starting at noon. All lessons will be (7) _____ (cancel) for the afternoon of that day. All parents (8)_____ (invite) to come. If bad weather is forecast, you (9)_____ (tell) and Sports Day (10)_____ (postpone) to the following week."

Will, may or must?

Read these sentences carefully. Then decide whether to put in *will*, *may* or *must*.
(10 marks)

1 This letter is urgent. It _____ be posted as soon as possible.

2 During a thunderstorm, don't shelter under a tree. It _____ be hit by lightning. If it is hit, you _____ be killed or seriously injured.

3 Be careful if you see an adder. It is a venomous snake with black zigzag marks on its top. Don't go near or touch an adder. If you do, you _____ be bitten. Then you _____ be taken to hospital. You _____ be given an antidote to fight the venom from the snake.

4   Check your bike before you go for a long ride. The brakes _____ be checked and the tyres _____ be pumped up if necessary.

5   When people return from a holiday overseas, their passports _____ be checked by an Immigration Officer. Then their luggage _____ be searched by a Customs Officer.

Active to passive

Change these sentences so that they contain *passive* verbs instead of active ones. Leave out the italic words. *(10 marks)*

1   *Somebody* stole Mr Jackson's car during the night.

2   Before the dentist drilled my tooth, *she* gave me an injection.

3   *Some workmen* pulled down that old factory last week.

4   *The strong wind* blew down two trees last night.

5   *Somebody* has just taken Mrs Sharpe to hospital.

6   *Two dustmen* collect our rubbish every Friday.

7   *People* grow a lot of apples in this part of the country.

8   *Sharks or other large fish* sometimes attack swimmers not far from the beach.

9   *The Mayor* will open the new school tomorrow.

10 *Several workmen* will redecorate our school during the holidays.

Official language

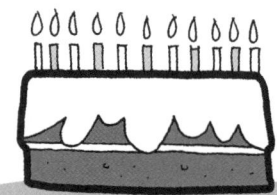

 **Key idea**

Formal and official documents have certain language features that distinguish them from informal writing.

Informal: first person (personal); colloquial/slang vocabulary; use of contractions; short, simple sentences; exclamations, questions

Formal: third person (impersonal); technical, subject-specific vocabulary; no contractions; complex sentences; statements

---

Len Benton sent his friend, Mary Evans, a fake formal letter from a firm of solicitors when she wanted to borrow his bicycle. Mary decided to continue the game with Len. She sent him this invitation to her birthday party.

> On behalf of Miss Mary Evans, we have very considerable pleasure in requesting the pleasure of your company at a sumptuous festive social gathering of young attractive females and boisterous males to celebrate the eleventh anniversary of her blessed nativity.
>
> Please be informed accordingly that this joyful event will take place at Miss Evans' ancestral place of residence at 462 Rowan Road on Saturday 25 April, commencing punctually at 4 p.m. and drawing to a close by 8 p.m.
>
> To enable us to make adequate preparations, we would greatly appreciate it if you would kindly get in touch with us and indicate whether or not you will be able to join all concerned in this celebration. Kindly let us know what you decide before noon on 21 April so that our plans may be finalised well in advance. Alternatively, you may prefer to make your decision known directly to Mary (by phone, email, fax or in person).
>
> We are asked to pass on to all guests Mary's particular request that presents should not be brought or sent.

What do they mean?

Find and underline the expressions in Mary's invitation that have these meanings.
(10 marks)

1 are happy	3 party	5 birthday	7 home	9 would like
2 to invite	4 children	6 note (verb)	8 finishing	10 everybody

In translation

Len's brother asked him what was in the letter from Mary. Pretend you are Len. Tell your brother – in everyday English – what the main points of the invitation are. *(10 marks)*

_____
_____
_____
_____
_____
_____

Keep it simple

Give the meaning of the expressions in italics. Use ordinary, everyday English that makes the meaning clear but uses fewer words. *(10 marks)*

1 Please *contact him in writing*. _____

2 Write your name here, *giving your surname and all given names*.
_____

3 *In the event that* you are unable to come, bring a note when you recover.
_____

4 Mike missed a lot of lessons at school *as a result* of illness.
_____

5 Ask a parent or *the person who is legally responsible for looking after you* to write a note to your teacher, explaining why you were absent.
_____

6 Peter cannot come today because he is *suffering from some illness*.
_____

7 The *man who has been accused of robbery but has not yet been tried or convicted* will give evidence tomorrow.
_____

8 Mr Macdonald is a farmer, so he would like to *wipe out and completely get rid of* all the rabbits on his farm.
_____

9 Your claim for compensation will be *studied in detail to ascertain all aspects of the problem*.
_____

10 You will be told *what is eventually decided by officials who look into your case*.
_____

Unit 10

Forming complex sentences 2

Key idea

subordinate clause   main clause   subordinate clause

After the party, *we all went straight home* *because it was late*.

There are different types of subordinate clauses. They are linked to the main clause with connectives.

Adding connectives

Put one of the following connectives in each blank space below. *(10 marks)*

if	after	before	although	when	so
while	despite	provided	so	that	

1. I have a poster that reminds me to wash my hands _____ I have a meal, and to clean my teeth _____ I have eaten anything.

2. _____ Mum agrees, we're going to have a barbecue this evening _____ it doesn't rain.

3. The house in Elm Street was too expensive and _____ my parents decided not to buy it _____ we all liked it very much

4. You can borrow these videos but let me have them back _____ Mary can watch them _____ she returns from holiday.

5. The fire started _____ men were carrying out repairs. It destroyed the whole building _____ the efforts of the firemen.

Punctuating complex sentences

Punctuate these sentences correctly. Don't forget to put in capital letters where necessary. *(10 marks – 2 marks for each correct sentence)*

1 we expected toms friend to come at 5 pm however he didnt arrive until 530

2 in the middle of lunch a boy rushed into the canteen shouting fire fire

3 I put my books away and turned off the light then I went to bed

4 when the phone rang maya picked it up expecting to hear her friends voice

5 the answer peter gave although partially correct was not the right one

Joining sentences

Join each group of sentences to make one sentence. You can change, add or omit words. *(10 marks – 2.5 marks for each correct sentence)*

1 The rain stopped. We played in the garden. The grass was still wet. We were quite chilly.

2 The girl won lots of money. She gave half of it to charity. She is Janet's cousin.

3 This is the ring. My aunt gave it to me. I was ten then. It is beautiful.

4 Uncle George is over fifty. He completed the marathon. He raised lots of money for charity.

Unit 11 — Making notes

Key idea

We make notes to extract the most important points from written words (such as information text) or spoken words (such as a telephone conversation or interview). We write them down in a shorter form.

Babysitting

You are babysitting for Mrs Done. You receive some phone calls and need to jot down notes so that you can write out messages for her. Make notes. *(10 marks)*

1. Is that Connie Jackson? Oh, well, maybe I could leave a message for her. My name is Peter Brown. I was going to call on her tomorrow at her office at about ten but something has come up, so I can't make it. Please ask her to phone my secretary at 099-438 tomorrow to fix another appointment. Thursday or Friday would be fine for me, ideally in the morning. Thanks. Goodbye.

2. Can I interest you in a good deal on double-glazing? This week we're offering … Oh, I see. Hmmm. Well, perhaps you'd tell her that Glunk Glass have this special offer next week, for seven days only. We're offering a discount of twenty-five per cent for two windows or more. If further details are needed, ask the lady to phone Andrew Brown at 047-738 any time. Thanks.

Customer services

You are learning the work in the Customer Services Department of a busy store. People phone, so you have to take notes and then tell the manager what the complaint is about. Read what these people said to you. Make notes. *(10 marks)*

1. My name's Ivy Trott. What's that? No, I'm not related to her. What I want to do is complain about the Milky Way Mousse. Don't get me wrong. I like them very much, but you never seem to have any in stock. What's happened? Are the staff eating them all? How come you've never got any on sale? Please ask somebody to order some more, pronto!

2   I want to complain about the tomatoes in your fruit and vegetable section. I usually buy a packet of six. Twice I've found that two of the tomatoes were bad underneath. They look all right on top but when you get them out – that's a different story. Maybe you could have a word with your order clerk or whoever does the ordering and change your supplier. I'll check up on them in the coming weeks and let you know if I see any improvement. I will be bringing back the two bad ones I bought this week and will expect a refund.

Local newspaper reporter

You are a reporter in the office of a local newspaper. You receive these phone calls. Make notes of the important points. *(10 marks)*

1   In the past week, six cars have been damaged by hooligans in Leo's car park. Each of them had a window broken. One had its tyres slashed. Three had the paintwork scratched badly. The damage occurs between about 10 p.m. and 6 a.m. I can tell you the names and addresses of a couple of louts who hang out there if you're interested.

2   You ought to investigate a house in Lufton Road. It's number 39 There's something fishy going on there. It's been empty for about six months, but recently the lights have been on and I've seen a lot of people coming and going with huge boxes at all hours of the day. There are often five or six lorries parked in the road at a time. There's a problem with burglary in our area at the moment. Perhaps the house is being used to store stolen goods.

Writing a summary

🔑 Key idea

A summary is a re-telling in a shorter number of words of something you have read or heard.
- Summaries require writing in complete sentences.
- Summaries should include the main idea and important points only.

One-word summaries

In each case, give one word that summarises the group of words below. *(10 marks)*

1. a place where water is stored so that it can be sent to homes
   _____

2. walking along slowly and hardly lifting the feet off the ground
   _____

3. a long hole through a hill, often for a railway line
   _____

4. a place where people can keep their money and earn interest
   _____

5. a man or woman who looks after sick or injured people
   _____

6. wet stuff that comes trickling down from the clouds
   _____

7. biting and biting and biting (when the food is tough)
   _____

8. not liking to be delayed or kept waiting for anything
   _____

9. taken into custody (by a police officer)
   _____

10. in a way showing considerable skill
    _____

Headlines

Make up five newspaper headlines (of not more than six words each). *(10 marks – 2 marks for each one)*

1. A mineshaft has opened under a house in a village near Durham, causing half the house to disappear down the shaft. Luckily, the owners were in the other half of the house and were not hurt – but they were shocked.
   _____

2. A large black animal, similar to a panther, has been seen by a farmer in a field near Taunton. Several sheep have been killed in the vicinity recently.
   _____

3. Cricketer Jason Foley has just scored 500 not out in a test match against Australia. He has earned a five-figure bonus for his achievement.
   _____

4. A girl, aged 12, fell at home, hit her head on a stone floor and became unconscious. Her mother dialled 999 but the ambulance did not arrive until an hour later. By that time, the girl was gravely ill. She died shortly after she was taken to hospital. Her parents were outraged and very angry at the delay.
   _____

5. A venomous spider was found in a bunch of grapes imported from South Africa. The purchaser spotted the spider and took it to a laboratory where it was examined and then killed. It was found to be extremely harmful. The store which sold the grapes has apologised and promised to inspect imports more thoroughly.
   _____

What can you remember?

Write a summary of each of the things below. Use a single sentence each time. Do not use more than twenty words in each sentence. *(10 marks – 2.5 marks for each sentence)*

1. A recent lesson which you enjoyed at school _____
   _____

2. What you did yesterday from 5 p.m. until the time you went to bed _____
   _____

3. The last television programme you watched _____
   _____

4. Your favourite book _____
   _____

Unit 13 Editing

Key idea

Editing involves reviewing and improving our own (or someone else's) writing to make it more effective.

Using more effective words

You are editing a composition written by a friend. Suggest two more effective words that could be used instead of the words in italics. Your words do not have to be synonyms of the italic words, but they should be suitable for the situation.

(10 marks – 0.5 mark for each suitable answer)

1. A group of children ran away in front of us. When we were nearly at the corner, a woman *came* out of her house. She was upset and waved her arms angrily at us.

   _____   _____

2. 'Go away! Get out of here!' she *said to* us *loudly*.

   _____   _____

   _____   _____

3. The policeman *looked* at us. His face *indicated* that trouble was coming.

   _____   _____

   _____   _____

4. The old man *moved* painfully towards the receptionist.

   _____   _____

5. Mary wore a *nice* outfit to her friend's party.

   _____   _____

6. The tornado *pulled apart* the town, leaving a trail of destruction behind it.

   _____   _____

7. The poor animal *moved* towards us on its three good legs as if *asking* us to help.

   _____   _____

   _____   _____

Correcting errors

The following sentences are taken from a report by a pupil about the school canteen. Edit the sentences by correcting any mistakes in them. Write out the sentences correctly. *(10 marks – 0.5 mark for each correction)*

1. In the coarse of our investigations, we watched pupils had lunch on sevral days.

2. We noticed that some pupil had to queue a long time before they could obtained there food.

3. We therefore suggest that there should be two seperate sessions for lunch, the younger children can eat 20 minutes earlier then the oldest pupils.

4. This will also prevent the food to becoming cold and will enable the servers to work more careful, they are all in favour of this change.

5. We asked each pupil to complete a questionaire about the food, we used the information from them to produce the lists in Apendix 3

6. The tables what the pupils sit at are to crowded, so we recommend that only six pupils sit at each table, this will be possible if we have two sessions instead of one.

Using headings

(10 marks)

A classmate prepared to write a report on her school canteen. She jotted down these points:

amount of food	crowding	behaviour of pupils	servers
tables	pupil satisfaction	quality of food	cooks
cost of food	seating	cleanliness/hygiene	taste
(un)healthy food	hours/time	queues	waste

She showed you her notes and asked you for your opinion on arranging the points.

1 Suggest **five** main headings under which most or all of the points can be put.

_____
_____
_____
_____
_____

The pupils in Miss Wilson's class asked her if they could have a class picnic, so she asked them to plan the arrangements for a picnic. One pupil wrote about the following points but did not put them under any headings or in any clear order.

date	bus/car/train/coach	music/songs	weather – alternative indoors
times	food	drinks	parents – inform, come?
place	games	cost	activities

2 Suggest **five** main headings for a plan for the picnic.

_____
_____
_____
_____
_____

Unit 14: Conditional sentences

🔑 Key idea

A conditional sentence says that one thing depends on another. Conditional sentences usually contain the words **if** or **unless**. The "if" or "unless" part of the sentence is a special type of subordinate clause called a **conditional clause**.

<u>*conditional clause*</u>   <u>*main clause*</u>
If you tickle me, I will laugh.

What happens?

Complete these sentences in any sensible way. They are about habitual (usual) actions. *(10 marks – 2 marks for each correct sentence)*

1. If you leave ice out of a fridge, _____

2. If a player hits another player during a game of football, _____
_____

3. If people find that they have mice in their home, _____
_____

4. If it rains while the sun is shining, _____

5. If I'm very thirsty during the night, _____

What will probably happen?

Put in the right form of the verbs in brackets. The sentences are about things that may, can or probably will happen in future. *(5 marks – 0.5 mark for each correct answer)*

1. If a young child _____ (play) with matches at home, he or she _____ (start) a fire.

2. If it rains on Saturday, our Sports Day _____ (postpone). Then it _____ (hold) on 23 June.

3. If you _____ (eat) too much food, you _____ (put) on weight.

4. If you both stand on that table at the same time, it _____ (probably collapse) and you _____ (break) something.

5. If the rain doesn't stop soon, all this area _____ (flood) and we _____ (force) to leave our home.

27

Giving advice

We can use **If I were you ...** to give advice:

If I were you,	I wouldn't eat so much.
	I wouldn't bother to answer that email.
	I would be honest about it.

What advice can you give these friends or relatives? *(10 marks – 2 marks for each suitable answer)*

1 Dave says he always feels tired in the morning. He admits that he rarely goes to bed before 11 p.m. because his parents let him stay up to watch films.

   _____

   _____

2 You are visiting an aunt with your brother or sister. You have both been offered a cup of coffee, but you have declined the coffee politely. Your brother or sister is not sure whether or not to try drinking it and asks your advice.

   _____

   _____

3 A friend says she has several unwanted jigsaw puzzles at home. She is not sure whether to take them to a charity shop or just to throw them away. What do you advise?

   _____

   _____

   _____

4 A friend's family are going to spend a few days in Paris during the holidays. They can't decide whether to go by rail, ferry or air. Your friend mentioned this to you and said, "What would you do?"

   _____

   _____

5 A friend goes to a different school from yours. He tells you that he has noticed that two older boys are bullying younger pupils and making them pay money nearly every day. He is not sure what, if anything, he should do. He has asked for your advice. What do you suggest?

   _____

   _____

Other ways of showing a condition

We can also show a condition by making sentences like these:

You can go	provided that	you return before dark.
You can play with them	as long as	you're back by 7.00 p.m.
It's all right for you to go	on condition that	you are not late home again.

Use the information in each pair of sentences to make one sentence using one of the connectives in the second column above. You can change, omit or add words.
(5 marks)

1. You can go to Tom's house. You must be back here by 8.00 p.m.

2. You can borrow my bike. You must return it on Saturday.

3. Tom can stay with us for the weekend. His parents must agree.

4. I'll help you. Don't argue all the time.

5. We can have a picnic on Saturday. The weather must be fine then.

Narrative writing

Key idea

The purpose of a narrative text is to tell a story. Although individual stories can be very different, they all have some common structural and language features.

Zangram by C. J. Salter: extract 1

Read this extract from *Zangram*. Then answer the questions below. *(10 marks)*

> 1   The Logan family pulled wearily into a deserted car park not far from Stonehenge. Jack Logan, exhausted after driving for nine hours, said to his wife, "I need a rest."
> "Good idea," his wife replied. "I told Sylvia we wouldn't be down 'til
> 5   noon."
> Jack Logan glanced in the rear-view mirror. His children, Daniel and Claire, were sleeping soundly. So he settled down and was soon asleep himself.
> Some time later, Claire stirred. The car seemed to be moving, but then
> 10   the movement stopped. She heard her dad snoring contentedly, and drifted back to sleep.
> On board Spacecraft 462, the doors closed and a message flashed back to Zangram, far beyond Earth's solar system: "Mission completed. 20 specimens including four bipeds in a metal shell." The spaceship rose silently
> 15   from a field near Stonehenge and hurtled off into space. It carried with it the Logan family, their car, two inquisitive dogs, a deeply resentful cat and other specimens destined for examination and display in the Zangram national zoo.

1   In paragraph one, which word repeats the idea expressed by "wearily"? *(1 mark)*

_____

2   What were Mrs Logan's exact words when she spoke to Sylvia? *(1 mark)*

_____

3   What is missing before "Good idea" (line 4)? Why has it been left out? *(2 marks)*

_____

4 What adverb could we use instead of each of the following? (The adverb need not have the same meaning as the given word, but it must fit the situation.) *(4 marks)*

   a) soundly (line 7) _____   c) silently (line 14) _____

   b) contentedly (line 10) _____   d) deeply (line 16) _____

5 a) What does "inquisitive" tell us about the dogs? b) Why was the cat "resentful"? *(2 marks)*

   _____

Zangram: extract 2

Read this continuation of *Zangram*. Then answer the questions about it.
(10 marks)

---

1   When the Logan family woke up, they discovered they were in a huge glass dome. They were unaware, however, of the battery of tests and examinations that the Zangrams had carried out on them over a period of several days.

5   Outside the dome, a crowd of Zangrams watched the family through one-way glass. A notice outside the dome said, when translated into English, "On loan from Planet 264S/36 for 30 days". Of course, the Logans knew nothing of this. They believed that somehow they had been kidnapped.

     "Well, at least we're alive," said Mrs Logan, trying to console her
10 children. "Sooner or later, we'll find out where we are and why we're here."

     She was right. They found out the next day when the Zangrams had finally solved the riddle of Earth language and began to communicate with them.

---

1 What happened to the Logan family before they were put on display? *(2 marks)*

   _____

2 Why does the writer start a new paragraph in three places after the first paragraph? Give a reason why each of the three paragraphs has been started. *(3 marks)*

   _____

   _____

   _____

3 How does the phrase that begins the second paragraph link it to the first paragraph? *(2 marks)*

   _____

4 What does the pronoun "this" in line 8 refer to? *(1 mark)*

_____

5 How does the writer create a dramatic effect at the beginning of the last paragraph? *(2 marks)*

_____

Zangram: extract 3

Now read extract 3 and answer the questions about it. *(10 marks)*

1   When the Logans woke up in the car park at Stonehenge, they were puzzled to find their car turned round. They knew something odd had happened, but what? They drove on to Cornwall in some confusion. Their bewilderment deepened when they finally reached the home of Jack's brother and rang the
5   doorbell. Tony Logan opened the door and stared at them in a mixture of astonishment and horror.
    "Where have you been?" he said at last. "We were expecting you a month ago! We checked with your neighbours. We even informed the police because …"
10   "A month ago!" echoed Jack Logan. "We agreed July 10th and here we are."
    Tony stared at his brother, trying to decide whether he was joking or not. "But today is August 10th," he pointed out. "Anyway, come in. You're welcome at any time – even when you're officially 'missing, presumed dead'."
    Mrs Logan and the children went in. Jack went back to the car to unpack
15   the luggage. What he saw in the boot proved that something very strange had occurred.

1 What is similar about the ways in which extracts 1, 2 and 3 end? *(2 marks)*

_____

2 "We even informed the police because …" Why does the author insert …? *(1 mark)*

_____

3 Find five *different* uses of capital letters in the extract. *(5 marks)*

_____

_____

4 Write a sentence saying what Mr Logan found in the boot. *(2 marks)*

_____

Unit 17 Describing past events

Key idea

The purpose of writing a recount is to tell about a past event. Recount texts have some common structural and language features that help to identify them.

Time connectives

Read the account of a football match below. Put in ten different linking words or expressions. Choose from those below. *(10 marks)*

right up to the final whistle	shortly afterwards	at the start of the game
within the first ten minutes	ten minutes later	for the rest of the first half
during the half-time break	at half-time	ten minutes from the end
	immediately	

(1)_____ yesterday, Newtown were confidently expected to beat Oldtown by at least two goals. Newtown forced two corners (2)_____, but failed to score. Oldtown struck back but Jordan's shot was wide. (3)_____, Ken Teale put Newtown one up when he headed home a cross from Ojuro. Play was restricted to the centre of the field (4)_____ with Newtown slightly superior. (5)_____ the score remained Newtown 1 – Oldtown 0

Newtown manager, Joe Kellick, gave his men a pep-talk (6)_____. The players responded with raids on the Oldtown goal, during which Ken Teale scored his second goal. (7)_____ Oldtown veteran, Paul Cranston, scored for Oldtown. Stung by this unexpected goal, Newtown launched another series of attacks (8)_____ and were rewarded when Ojuro scored Newtown's third goal.

(9)_____ Tom Baxter shot wide for Oldtown. Defences dominated the game (10)_____.

Final score: Newtown 3 – Oldtown 1

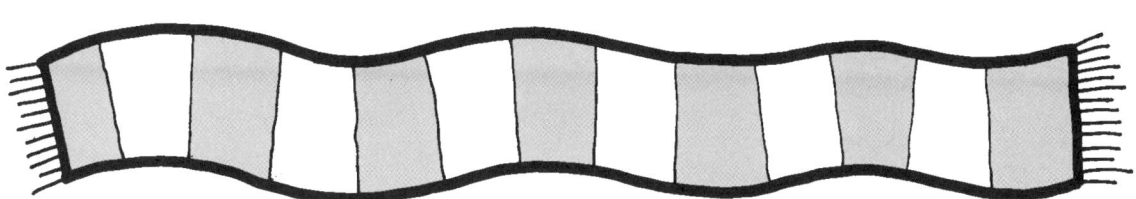

33

Exploring language

Read 'Hot water' and then answer the questions about it. *(20 marks)*

Hot water

1   Sue went to visit her grandfather, aged 90, in a remote rural district. Grandad cooked a very tasty lunch. However, when Sue put the plates and cutlery on the table, she noticed some tiny brown specks on her plate. She studied the plate thoughtfully for a few moments.

5   "Grandad," she asked hesitantly. "Are you … Are these plates clean?"

"Of course they are," Grandad replied quickly. "They're as clean as hot water can get them. That's for sure. Enjoy your meal and don't worry about the plates."

In the evening, Sue helped Grandad to prepare supper. She was hungry and
10 was just about to put the food on the plates when she saw a thin piece of something on one of the plates. It looked like scrambled egg.

"Grandad," she said firmly. "Are you absolutely sure these plates are clean?"

"No doubt about it," Grandad said with a smile. "They're as clean as hot
15 water can make them. I can guarantee that."

A few minutes later, a neighbour approached Grandad's house. Immediately his dog started to bark furiously. Grandad shouted angrily at the dog, "Cut that out, Hotwater! No more barking! Go and lay down! It's only Jim. You know him."

20 "I call her 'Hotwater'," Grandad explained to Sue, "because she always gets me into trouble."

"Ugh!" Sue thought. "I wonder if … I think I've been had."

"Grandad," she said quietly, "I'll wash the dishes tonight."

1   a) Underline any ten adjectives in the passage. *(5 marks)*

    b) Choose six of the adjectives and give words opposite in meaning to them. *(3 marks)*

    _____   _____

    _____   _____

    _____   _____

2   Choose three verbs used in the past tense in the passage. Write them down and then write the present and future tenses of each. *(3 marks)*

    _____

    _____

    _____

3   At the end of the third sentence, what one word can we insert after "plate" to turn the following sentence into a subordinate clause?_____ *(1 mark)*

4   Suggest a reason why Sue was hesitant when she first asked Grandad if the plates were clean? *(1 mark)*

    _____

5   Complete the sentence. *(1 mark)*

    "In line 6, the writer uses 'as … as' to_____

6   a) Write down any six adverbs in the passage. *(3 marks)*

    _____   _____

    _____   _____

    _____   _____

  b) Choose any four of the adverbs and write down words opposite in meaning to them. *(2 marks)*

7   What did Sue mean when she said, "I think I've been had"? *(1 mark)*

    _____

35

unit 18 Giving instructions

Key idea

Instructions, directions and descriptions of procedures all have to be written clearly and concisely so they are easy to follow. Features such as sequenced and numbered steps, imperative verbs and sequencing connectives are common to this type of writing.

Checklist

Paul wrote the following checklist for maintaining his bike. Read it and then answer the questions about it. *(15 marks)*

> Checklist for maintaining bicycles
> 1 Check <u>brake</u> cables. Do brake blocks make good contact with rims of wheels?
> 2 Is <u>bell</u> fastened firmly? Does it work properly?
> 3 Check if front and rear <u>lights</u>. Replace battry or check dynamo if necessary.
> 4 <u>Chain</u> – tighten and see if any oil is needed.
> 5 <u>Saddle</u> – make sure it is at the right height and comfortable.
> 6 <u>Carrier</u> – check that nuts holding carrier are not lose. Tighten?
> 7 Check nuts holding <u>wheels</u> in place. Tighten or replace if necessary.
> 8 Check air in <u>tyres</u>; check for slow punctures.
> 9 Grease or oil any points that need lubricating, e.g. wheel <u>axils</u>.
> 10 Check that <u>tyre valves</u> are working properly.
> 11 Buy <u>padlock</u> with at least two keys. Get extra keys cut?

1 In step 2, are "firmly" and "properly" adjectives or adverbs?
   _____ *(2 marks)*

2 In step 3, what words are missing from the first sentence?
   _____ *(2 marks)*

3 How could Paul do step 5? _____ *(2 marks)*

4 Find four misspelt words and correct them. *(4 marks)*

   _____   _____

   _____   _____

5 Rewrite step 2 as a single statement with an imperative verb. *(2 marks)*

   _____

6 Which two steps could you combine so that there are only ten steps? *(2 marks)*

_____

7 What is the purpose of step 11? *(1 mark)*

_____

Defrosting a freezer

Rewrite Gran's instructions for how to defrost a freezer. Set them out in the right order using no more than ten steps. Leave out points that are not necessary.
(15 marks)

> Well, of course, you have to make sure that you don't make a mess in the kitchen. We don't want any water left on the floor to make the place slippery. That's how Grandad broke a leg a few years ago. Get a few old towels (there are plenty at the bottom of the airing-cupboard) and take them to the freezer. Oh, yes, you'll need a pail or a saucepan to put the water in. Put one of the towels on the floor in front of the freezer to catch the drips. Now, where was I? Ah, yes, empty the freezer. There are only a couple of packets in it now. Stick them in the fridge. Turn off the electricity. Open the freezer wide. Put a couple of towels inside to soak up the water. If you're in a hurry, put a bowl of hot water on a shelf in the freezer. It will help to thaw out the ice. You can poke any pieces of ice free if you like but it's not necessary.
>
> Leave the freezer door open and just be patient. When the ice has all gone, wring out the towels. Clean and dry the freezer. Get rid of any water. Then put the packets back in the freezer and turn it on. Easy!

Unit 19 Writing reports

🔑 Key idea

Report texts present information on a subject. They describe things as they are. They often feature present-tense verbs, descriptive adjectives and adverbs, and headings and subheadings.

The breakfast report

(10 marks)

1. "Write a report about breakfast in your family," said the teacher to Paul's class. If you were in the class, how would you arrange your ideas? Think of headings for three paragraphs. *(3 marks)*

   _____
   _____
   _____

> Breakfast by Paul
> We have three different kinds of breakfast, classified according to how it is eaten.
> My favourite is a "sitting-down" breakfast. It is a leisurely event on Saturday and Sunday because I do not have to get up early. It includes cereal, fried eggs, beans, mushrooms, toast and jam and a big glass of orange juice.
> A "standing-up" breakfast involves a drink, toast and a piece of fruit. I usually have this on school days because I have less time.
> When I forget to set the alarm and am late for school, I have to have an "on-the-move" breakfast. I shoot out of the house, buy a chocolate bar and eat it before the bell rings.

2. Write paragraph headings for Paul's report above. *(3 marks)*

   _____
   _____
   _____

3. What part of speech is each of these words as it is used in Paul's report? *(4 marks)*
   a) classified _____ b) leisurely _____
   c) usually _____ d) shoot _____

The rodent report

This is part of a report on squirrels, written by Sally, age 11 Read it and then answer the questions about it. *(10 marks)*

Grey squirrels

Where they came from

Grey squirrels were brought to Britain from America many years ago and kept in zoos. Some excaped and spread to both rural and urban areas. They have now driven red squirrels away.

_____

They prefer to eat seeds, berries and especially nuts, so they can often be found near oak, beech and other nut trees. However, they also eat birds' eggs and baby birds. Therefore, the presents of squirrels often leads to the absence of birds since they cannot nest safely.

How they behave

Grey squirrels are active during the day and do not hibernate in winter. They are naturaly shy, but not when it comes to food. In some towns, squirrels in parks are so tame that they will take peanuts, if offered, from people's hands.

The problems they cause

Grey squirrels (in fact, all kinds of squirrels) can be pests. They raid berries and other fruit from bushes and trees in poeple's gardens. They also gnaw and eat bark, which leads to the death of trees.

---

1. a) Circle the passive verb in the first paragraph. *(1 mark)*
   b) Why is the verb not active? *(1 mark)* _____

2. Fill in the missing subheading for the second paragraph. *(2 marks)*

3. Draw a box around each of the connectives in the second paragraph. (Do not include "and".) *(2 marks)*

4. Find the four misspelled words in the report. Draw a line through each one and write the correctly spelled word above. *(2 marks)*

5. In the last sentence of the third paragraph, underline the main clause once and the subordinate clause twice. *(2 marks)*

Write a worm report

(10 marks)

Here are some notes about worms.
1 Think of four different headings under which you could group the notes.
2 Then write a four-paragraph report using the notes.

- Do not like light
- Eat dead leaves and soil
- Has complete digestive system
- Help plants to grow
- Live underground
- Long, soft bodies with head and tail end
- Make tunnels to move about
- No bones, eyes, legs
- Soil leaves body making worm "casts"
- Useful creatures – tunnels bring air to soil
- Use muscles and hairs on skin to move
- Take nutrients from soil as it passes through body

WORMS

Paragraph 1 heading:_____

Paragraph 2 heading:_____

Paragraph 3 heading:_____

Paragraph 4 heading:_____

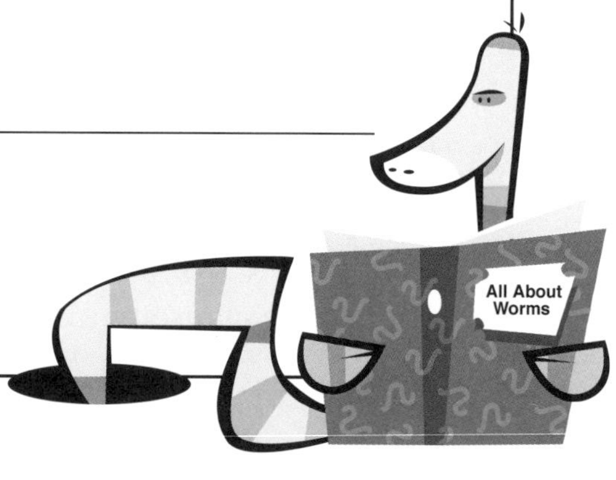

Unit 20

Persuasive writing

🔑 Key idea

Persuasive writing aims to influence the reader towards a particular opinion. It often uses emotional words, figurative devices and imperative verbs.

Email scam

Mrs Stone received this email, which is full of mistakes. Fortunately, she knew it was not from her bank at all, but an attempt by someone to find out her details illegally. Read it and answer the questions. *(10 marks)*

```
Subject: Confirm your details to avoid immediate cancellation to your
account.
Yesterday the bank have a failure of its software this resulted in a
lost of customer data. To help you to avoid from fraud, kindly connect
with the link below to confirm your account registration data, this is
obligatory to protect your account.
Please do not answer to this message. Fill in the form "Confirmation
of Acount Details".
```

1 Which words in the "subject" are meant to frighten the receiver? *(1 mark)*

2 Find an incorrect verb tense. Explain why it is wrong and correct it. *(2 marks)*

3 Find two places where punctuation is wrong or missing. Correct them. *(2 marks)*

4 Find and correct four expressions in which prepositions are used wrongly. *(2 marks)*

5 Find and correct two spelling mistakes. *(2 marks)*

6 Why does the sender of the email put in the sentence, "This is obligatory to protect your account"? *(1 mark)*

**The mighty T-watch is here:
hep, handy, helpful!**

It's COOL and it could be yours!

On one side, it's a watch.
No need to look at it.

Press the button and it tells you the time. Now that's really something – but there's more!

On the other side? A nifty recorder. Up to 10 minutes talktime. No need to take notes.

**Move up to the in-crowd!
ORDER NOW
before they're all snapped up.**

"I love it!" says pop star Kati Lane.

Football legend, Mike O'Shea:
"I wouldn't be without mine!"

An advertisement

Read the advertisement above and then answer these questions. *(10 marks)*

1   Which slang words in the advertisment mean "up-to-date, fashionable"? *(1 mark)*

2   What figurative device is used in the second line? *(1 mark)*

3   Why is "COOL" put in capital letters? *(1 mark)*

4   "On the other side? A nifty recorder." Explain why the writer doesn't use complete sentences. *(2 marks)*

5   Why does the advertiser use the word "nifty" instead of "clever"? *(1 mark)*

6   Explain the purpose of the pictures. *(2 marks)*

7   Give one example each of two different verb forms used in the advertisement. *(1 mark)*

8   In the first draft of this advertisement, the advertiser wrote : "Keep up with the in-crowd". Why did she change this to "Move up to the in-crowd"? *(1 mark)*

Getting involved

Miss Benson's class wrote to their local council following three traffic accidents near their school. Read their first draft below and then answer the questions.
(10 marks)

> In the passed six months, there have been three horrific traffic acidents near our school, each time somebody was knocked down by a speeding motorist. We beg the Council to do something to make Bridge Street safer.
>
> We would like to recommend four crucial measures. First of all, we hope the Council can put some speed bumps in the road to slow down traffic. Secondly, we need a pedestran crossing outside our school. Thirdly, it would be a good idea to errect warning sines at each end of Bridge Street, finally, we think that cars should not be aloud to park outside our school for longer than 15 minutes during 8–9 a.m. and 3–4 p.m. on school days.

1 Why do the children mention accidents in their letter? *(1 mark)*

2 Give two examples of powerful, emotive words in the letter. Why do the children use them? *(2 marks)*

3 Find and correct six spelling mistakes in the draft letter. *(3 marks)*

4 Find two places where a comma should be replaced by a full stop. *(1 mark)*

5 Find a passive verb in the first paragraph. *(1 mark)*

6 List the sequencing connectives used in the second paragraph. *(1 mark)*

7 How might the children revise the layout of the second paragraph so that their suggestions are clearer? *(1 mark)*

Unit 21 Writing discussion texts

Key idea

Discussion texts give a balanced presentation of all the various positions that are held about an issue or topic – for example, both sides of an argument.

Television: points of view

"Does television do more harm than good?" Read the first draft of what one pupil wrote and then answer the questions about it. *(10 marks)*

1 Most television shows have a bad influence to viewers, especially young ones. They use swear words and bad language most of the time. Violence is common in "soaps" and are regarded as a model or example to teenagers.

On the other hand, documentries are both educational and intresting. There is always
5 something new for viewers to learn as long as they can stay awake. Oddly enough, the cartoons are usually OK. They are always amusing without setting a bad example. Sports programmes are also worth watching and do not cause no harm or offence.

Maybe the only fair answer to the question is that the affect of TV depends upon the individual. If you have firm principals, you can always chose wisely. I hope that television
10 channels will clean up their act, but I won't hold my breathe waiting for that to happen.

1 What more accurate word should the writer use instead of "most" in lines 1 and 2? *(1 mark)*

2 In lines 1 and 3, replace "to" with correct prepositions. *(2 marks)*

3 Explain and correct the error of agreement in the third sentence. *(1 mark)*

4 Explain and correct the error in the last sentence of the second paragraph. *(1 mark)*

5 Correct six spelling mistakes in the last two paragraphs. *(3 marks)*

6 Is the writer's discussion well-balanced? Explain your answer. *(2 marks)*

Maths – or no maths?

"Should children be allowed to decide whether they want to study maths or not?" Read the first draft of what one pupil wrote and then answer the questions about it. *(10 marks)*

1 Some people say that we do not need maths in our daily lifes because calculators and computers can give us all the answers. I don't agree to that because sometimes if we don't know any maths it is easy for crooks to cheat us. Also we need maths whenever we buy or sell anything and maybe we have no calculator available.

5 On the other hand, it is true that algebra and geometry can be too difficult to some children and they become confused and fed up. Then they may even hate the subject and start to behave badly at school. Perhaps the right thing to do is to make basic maths compulsery up to, say, the age of 14 and to make it optional after that. If somebody is no good at maths (even when he or she tries very hard), it is a waist of time to force the
10 person to continue to study the subject.

1 Find and correct four spelling errors: two in each paragraph *(2 marks)*

2 Correct the mistakes in the use of prepositions in lines 2 and 5 *(1 mark)*

3 What more formal words could the writer use instead of "crooks" (line 3) and "fed up" (line 6)? *(1 mark)*

4 How many points for each side of the argument does the writer give? What are they? *(4 marks)*

5 Do you agree with the writer's conclusion? Give reasons for your answer. *(2 marks)*

Should it be a crime to kill any wild animal?

(10 marks)

Put a suitable word in each blank space. *(7 marks – 0.5 mark for each correct answer)*

I am in favour of protecting wild animals, but there (1)_____ two main reasons (2)_____ I do not think it (3)_____ be a crime to kill any wild animal. Firstly, sometimes it is (4)_____ to kill wild animals such as mice, rats and rabbits. (5)_____ we do not kill some of them, they will increase (6)_____ cause serious problems. A (7)_____ reason is that sometimes wild animals, such (8)_____ boars, foxes, badgers and deer, increase and (9)_____ a threat to farmers. Then it is necessary to kill some of (10)_____.

We must also remember (11)_____ some farmers keep cattle, sheep, deer, goats and (12)_____ animals for their milk or meat. Are these wild animals? If somebody kills a wild pony on Dartmoor (13)_____ that a crime? As I said earlier, I think some wild animals should be protected, but making it a crime to kill one is not the (14)_____ way of doing it.

- **Do you think it should be a crime to kill wild animals? Give two reasons for your answer.** *(3 marks)*

_____
_____
_____
_____
_____

Unit 22

Investigating English expressions

Key idea

Investigating language is the best way to find out how it works.

American English

(16 marks)

Americans speak English, but many of their words differ from British English. Do you know what they're talking about? Put the right British word by each American word below. *(8 marks – 0.5 mark for each correct answer)*

> taxi   pavement   sweets   dummy (for a baby)   nappy   trousers
> autumn   boot (of a car)   lorry   curtains   petrol   sweet biscuits
> lift   handbag   queue   tap (for water)

1 cab _____

2 line _____

3 fall _____

4 truck _____

5 diaper _____

6 purse _____

7 candy _____

8 pants _____

9 trunk (of a car) _____

10 gas(oline) _____

11 pacifier _____

12 cookies _____

13 faucet _____

14 sidewalk _____

15 drapes _____

16 elevator _____

Now find out for yourself the British words for these American words. *(8 marks)*

17 drugstore _____   21 vacation _____

18 closet _____   22 garbage _____

19 stove _____   23 movies _____

20 hood (of a car) _____   24 buck (money) _____

Investigating idioms

Put the right idiom on each line below. *(14 marks)*

- a Tartar
- eyewash
- a close shave
- a mouthpiece
- a square peg in a round hole
- a rough diamond
- a pig in a poke
- a fool's paradise
- a blank cheque
- a fly in the ointment
- a red herring
- a hornets' nest
- soft soap
- a white lie

1. A _____ is an untrue statement which is made for good reasons, for example to protect an innocent person.

2. _____ is something (usually a statement) meant to deceive people or hide something wrong.

3. _____ is a person who is very difficult to deal with even if you have some advantage over them. Many years ago, if you captured this person in a battle, he would prove a troublesome prisoner.

4. _____ is something which is meant to deceive you, perhaps by making you look in the wrong direction when trying to solve a problem.

5. _____ is permission to do as you like, for example to spend as much money as you like because the cheque has been signed but no amount has been put in.

6. If you spend a lot of time dreaming about winning a lottery, you may live in _____, thinking about something nice which will never happen.

7. If you buy _____, you buy something (such as a pig tied up in a sack) before you have had a chance to inspect it.

8. _____ is flattery.

9. _____ is somebody who appears tough or lacking in manners, but is really very kind and generous.

10. If a person is in a job that does not suit him or her, we may say that the person is _____.

11. _____ is an obstacle to a plan.

12. Sometimes we call a narrow escape _____.

13. _____ is somebody who speaks on behalf of another person or organisation, often to give excuses or reasons for an action.

14. _____ is a source of possible trouble because if you interfere you may create a worse situation.

Key Grammar is a brand new resource, specifically planned to cover all the key grammar objectives in self-contained units of work. The pupil books feature:

- clear, progressive units covering all key learning objectives
- plenty of practice and consolidation work
- opportunities to challenge and extend children's learning
- a clear mark scheme
- exercises in an appropriate context, with engaging illustrations

The workbooks provide activities for additional practice, differentiation, and homework. The important language skills coverage in **Key Grammar** is complemented by two associated series:
Key Comprehension and **Key Spelling** – up-to-date and engaging resources which reinforce key teaching points and enable children to practise, consolidate and extend their learning. For further information about **Key Comprehension** and **Key Spelling** call our Customer Services Department on **(+44) (0)1865 888000**.

ISBN 978-0-602206-85-7

Author: **Alan Etherton**

Ginn is an imprint of Pearson education Limited, a company incorporated in England and Wales, having its registered office at Edinburgh Gate, Harlow, Essex, CM20 2JE.
Registered company number: 872828

www.ginn.co.uk
Help and support for teachers plus the widest range of education solutions

© Harcourt Education Limited 2005

This book is copyright and reproduction of the whole or part without the publishers' written permission is prohibited.

Key Grammar Workbook 4
ISBN: 978 0602 20685 7
Level 4 Easy Order Pack: 978 0602 20651 2
Level 4 Workbook 6 Pack: 978 0602 20648 2

First published 2005

16
13

Cover illustration by Pet Gotohda
Cover design by Tom Cole
Designed by Nicki Wise, Te Marama Design
Illustrations by David Semple, Gary Swift, Andrew Painter

Printed and bound in China (GCC/13)

# Grammar Workbook 4

Contents

Unit 1	Word classes	page 2
Unit 2	Using standard English	page 4
Unit 3	Active and passive verbs 1	page 6
Unit 4	Connectives	page 8
Unit 5	Forming complex sentences 1	page 10
Unit 6	Punctuation	page 12
Unit 8	Active and passive verbs 2	page 14
Unit 9	Official language	page 16
Unit 10	Forming complex sentences 2	page 18
Unit 11	Making notes	page 20
Unit 12	Writing a summary	page 22
Unit 13	Editing	page 24
Unit 14	Conditional sentences	page 27
Unit 16	Narrative writing	page 30
Unit 17	Describing past events	page 33
Unit 18	Giving instructions	page 36
Unit 19	Writing reports	page 38
Unit 20	Persuasive writing	page 41
Unit 21	Writing discussion texts	page 44
Unit 22	Investigating English expressions	page 47

Unit 1: Word classes

Key idea

Words are categorised in classes according to the jobs they do in a sentence: noun, pronoun, verb, adjective, adverb, preposition, conjunction and interjection. Words can belong to more than one class.

Work it out

Give one-word answers. *(10 marks)*

1. Which proper noun is the name of the Italian capital? _____
2. Which adjective is the opposite of "wise"? _____
3. Which collective noun means "a lot of (birds flying) together"? _____
4. Which verb means "to tremble with cold or fear"? _____
5. Which pronoun is the opposite of "no one"? _____
6. Which proper noun is the name of the shortest month of the year? _____
7. Which adverb is the opposite of "rarely"? _____
8. What is the second part of the conjunction "not only…"? _____
9. What adverb can we form from "skill"? _____
10. Which verb means to "make longer"? _____

Which word?

Ring or underline the right word in the brackets. *(10 marks)*

1. It was dark, so we couldn't see (nothing, anything) clearly.
2. Would you mind (to wait, waiting) a few minutes?
3. There (are, is) more than one way of solving this problem.
4. Where (are, is) the rest of the players?
5. The change in the plan will not have a great deal of (affect, effect) on us.
6. Don't be so (impatience, impatient), John!
7. Between you and (I, me), I think Margaret is quite right to be suspicious.
8. This photo is different (than, from) that one.
9. We watched the marathon, but we did not (took, take) part in it.
10. Your new bike is much better than (Paul's, Pauls').

Classify it

Read this passage from *Nicholas Nickleby* by Charles Dickens. Place each of the underlined words under the correct heading in the grid below. *(10 marks – 0.5 mark for each correctly placed word)*

Dotheboy's Hall <u>was</u> not a hall at all, <u>but</u> a bare and dirty room with a <u>couple</u> of windows, in which most of the glass was broken. There were a few old <u>rickety</u> desks, <u>cut</u> and notched, and inked and damaged, in <u>every</u> possible way; a detached desk for <u>Squeers</u>; and another <u>for</u> his assistant. The ceiling was supported, like <u>that</u> of a barn, by cross beams and rafters; and the walls were so stained that it was impossible to tell <u>whether</u> they had ever been painted or whitewashed.

But the pupils! How his last hopes <u>faded</u> as <u>he</u> looked <u>around</u>! Pale and haggard faces of old men, boys of stunted growth, and others whose long thin legs would <u>hardly</u> carry their <u>stooping</u> bodies, all <u>crowded</u> together; there were the bleary eye, the hare-lip, the crooked foot, and every problem arising from <u>cruelty</u> and neglect. There were little faces which should have been handsome, darkened with the scowl of suffering; there were vicious-faced boys, brooding like prisoners in jail; <u>and</u> there were children <u>who</u> were weeping <u>with</u> loneliness…

nouns	
pronouns	
verbs	
adjectives	
adverbs	
prepositions	
conjunctions	

Using standard English

 **Key idea** ••••••••••••••••••••••••••••••••••

We can use non-standard English in speech, but we must use standard English in formal written work.

Does it agree? ••••••••••••••••••••••••••••••••

Underline the subject each time. (It may be a single word or a group of words.) Then circle the right word in the brackets so that the verb agrees with its subject.
(14 marks)

1 How much of the information in newspaper reports or radio and television news reports (are, is) completely accurate?

2 According to a report on television, a reward of several thousand pounds (has, have) been offered for information leading to the arrest of the robbers.

3 The driver of the bus – together with two of the passengers – (was, were) slightly injured in the accident.

4 (Is, Are) there any mud on your shoes?

5 The number of flights from London to Spain (have, has) risen in recent years because more people like to spend a holiday on the Spanish coast.

6 There (is, are) a number of reasons why people prefer to spend their holiday abroad. The main attraction is the better climate overseas.

7 What a nuisance! All the traffic (has, have) stopped. There must have been an accident somewhere ahead of us.

8 Before the play started, a member of the cast peeped through the curtains and said, "Oh, good! The audience (is, are) a really big one tonight. There are no empty seats."

9 Everybody in our class (want, wants) to join in the picnic, don't they?

10 How long (has, have) all this rubbish been lying here?

11 As a result of a change in the law, the poor (is, are) likely to be better off.

12 A good standard of numeracy (is, are) necessary in many jobs.

13 At least a third of those players (is, are) from foreign countries.

14 The majority of the pupils in our class (does, do) not come to school in a car.

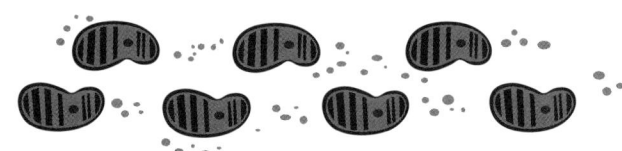

Choose the right word

Ring or underline the right words in the brackets. *(8 marks)*

1 This shop doesn't sell cosmetics (or, nor) health foods.

2 My sister doesn't like garlic and (so, nor) do I.

3 Sometimes people are not sure where to keep their money. If they hide (them, it) at home, there is always a risk of burglary.

4 The manager told his staff that he hadn't (no, any) intention of resigning.

5 John did not feel very well at the start of the cross-country race, and he felt much (worse, worser) at the end.

6 After the show, my friend and (me, I) bought some chips and ate (it, them) on the way home.

7 We need somebody to check all the electrical (equipment, equipments) before we turn on the computer and heating.

8 Our visit to Scandinavia (maybe, may be) described as a tour rather than a holiday.

Make it formal

Write more formal expressions that we can use instead of the italic words. *(8 marks)*

1 That's a *lousy* idea. _____

2 There's a rumour that their business is *on the rocks*. _____

3 All the *kids* in my class agree with me. _____

4 I haven't got *nothing* special to tell you. _____

5 The man said he didn't know *no one* with that name. _____

6 The fact that he is guilty *sticks out like a sore thumb*. _____

7 This hairstyle is gradually *catching on*. _____

8 *How come* you're not at school today? _____

Unit 3 Active and passive verbs 1

Key idea

Verbs can be in the **active** or **passive** voice.

A dangerous job

Write in the *passive* Simple Present form of the verbs in brackets. *(12 marks)*

In Malaysia, rubber (1)_____ (grow) on many estates. At dawn, rubber-tappers start work. Many of them are women and they know that their work can be dangerous. Sometimes tappers (2)_____ (attack) by a tiger. When they bend down to tap a tree, they (3)_____ (sometimes mistake) for a wild animal and attacked by a hungry tiger.

Tappers start work before the sun rises. First, a cut (4)_____ (make) in a mature tree. A tin or half a coconut shell (5)_____ (fasten) to the tree. It (6)_____ (use) to collect latex from the cut. The tapper cuts many trees. Then he or she returns to the first tree. Latex in the tin (7)_____ (empty) into a pail which (8)_____ (take) to the small "factory" on the estate. Chemicals (9)_____ (add) to the latex and mixed in well. Later on, the latex (10)_____ (squeeze) into sheets which (11)_____ (hang) in a smoke-filled hut. Finally, the sheets of rubber (12)_____ (tie) up in bales, ready for export to other countries.

A gas leak

Put in the *passive* form of the verbs in brackets. Use *has/have been + a past participle* each time. *(10 marks)*

One evening Mrs Wilson (Mrs W) was on her way home from work. She got off a bus and started to walk the 200 metres to her home. As she walked round a corner, she was surprised to see a crowd of people outside a wrecked house. There were fire-engines and police cars there too. Mrs Wilson's friend, Mrs Johnson (Mrs J), was in the crowd.

Mrs W: What's the matter? What's happened?

Mrs J: There was a gas leak. That house (1)_____ (wreck) completely.

Mrs W: (2)_____ anybody _____ (injure)?

Mrs J: Yes, two people (3)_____ (hurt). They (4)_____ (take) to hospital already.

Mrs W: What are the fire-engines doing here?

Mrs J: There was a small fire but it (5)_____ (bring) under control. The gas company (6)_____ (inform), so men are coming to repair the pipe. A lot of debris (7)_____ (hurl) across the road, so the windows in those houses (8)_____ (break). The people in those houses (9)_____ (evacuate). There were some elderly people in that old folks' home over there. They (10) _____ (move) to another home temporarily.

Mrs W: Is there anything we can do to help?

Mrs J: No, I don't think so.

In trouble

Put in the *passive* future form of the verbs in brackets. Use *will be* + *a past participle*. *(8 marks)*

Paul's friend, Mike, was sent off during a football match for hitting an opponent. Now Paul is asking his dad, a referee, what will happen to Mike.

Paul: Will Mike get into trouble?

Dad: Yes, I'm afraid he will. I'm sure he (1)_____ (charge) with hitting an opponent. Then he (2)_____ (ask) to attend a hearing before the Disciplinary Committee. He (3)_____ (tell) what he is charged with.

Paul: What will happen after that?

Dad: He (4)_____ (give) a chance to listen to the referee's report and ask any questions. Then he (5)_____ (invite) to make his statement and admit the charge or try to deny it.

Paul: I don't think he will deny it because everybody saw what happened. What will the Committee do?

Dad: Well, Mike (6)_____ (inform) of the decision in writing. It is probable that he (7)_____ (ban) for a few months. If he has a bad record, he (8)_____ (fine) as well, I should think.

Unit 4 Connectives

🔑 Key idea

Connectives are words and phrases that are used to link different parts of a text. They can join words, phrases, clauses, sentences and paragraphs.

Types of connectives

Underline the connectives in the sentences below. Then put them under the correct heading in the grid. *(10 marks)*

1. Paul decided to buy the bicycle although it was expensive.
2. We can go out when the rain stops.
3. Mary stuck a stamp on the envelope and then she posted the invitation.
4. Following my operation, I developed an infection in the wound.
5. We can go for a picnic on Saturday if the weather is good.
6. Mike can't go out to play now because he hasn't finished his homework yet.
7. You can go to London by train or you can travel on the express bus.
8. Our new house is bigger than our old one. Moreover, it has a large garden.
9. Most people like Susan, but I think she is rather conceited.
10. Despite having a terrible cold, the soprano performed her solo.

Addition	Time	Cause and effect	Opposition

Connective starters

Complete each sentence in a suitable way to show that you understand the connective. *(10 marks)*

1 We'll have to wait here until _____

2 If you eat too much, _____

3 We couldn't move the wardrobe because _____

4 Although it snowed last night, _____

5 In spite of the cold weather, _____

6 Kate is very fond of animals, so _____

7 Choose your sweets and then _____

8 I forgot to set the alarm. As a result, _____

9 The game started on time despite _____

10 I often eat fish. However, _____

Choosing connectives

Ring or underline the right word in the brackets. *(10 marks)*

1 We can go there by taxi. (Alternately, Alternatively) we can take the bus.

2 (Despite, In spite) the discount, Mrs Lee decided not to buy the car.

3 We had to leave our house when a pipe burst. Now we're waiting for the workmen to complete the repairs. In the (while, meantime), we're staying with my grandparents.

4 The team has succeeded because the owner of the club is a billionaire. (Nevertheless, Furthermore) it has one of the best managers in Europe.

5 Crocodiles have no predators to attack them. (Consequently, Subsequently) they manage to live for many years.

6 Trees can spread their seeds in many ways. (Meanwhile, For example,) sycamore seeds have "wings" to help them fly away from the parent tree.

7 We don't agree with Paul's plan. On the (other hand, contrary), we think it could be disastrous for the club.

8 His plan contains several faults. (Nevertheless, Similarly) it contains some good points.

9 You ought to buy yourself a watch (instead of, in spite of) borrowing mine.

10 Most shops have security cameras (providing, so that) they can catch thieves.

unit 5 Forming complex sentences 1

🔑 Key idea

Complex sentences are made up of more than one clause.
The clauses can be joined in different ways.

Completing sentences

**Complete these sentences in any sensible way.
Draw a ring round the connecting words.** *(10 marks)*

1 A library is a place where _____

2 There was a hidden cottage where_____

3 Don't forget to turn the lights off when _____

4 People go to a dentist when _____

5 Plants will usually grow well if _____

6 Traffic police may stop a motorist if _____

7 Mary had the flu last week, so _____

8 Paul could not hear what people were saying on television, so ____
    _____

9 You can go to your friend's house now, provided that _____
    _____

10 You can borrow my bike if you like, provided that _____
    _____

What and where?

Complete each sentence by saying *what* people are doing and *where* they are doing it. Start with a present participle (an –ing word) *(10 marks)*

   Example: We watched some men **repairing** a pipe in the road near our home.

1 Ashra heard two women _____

2 When I came out of my house, I noticed a man _____
    _____

3 When we reached the beach, we saw some fishermen _____
    _____

4   Before we entered the park, we stopped to watch some boys _____
    _____

5   When Sue looked out of the window, she saw a blackbird _____
    _____

6   Last night on television we watched some girls _____
    _____

7   After a few minutes, the fox came to a field and was happy to see some lambs
    _____

8   Mr Evans woke up during the night when he heard somebody _____
    _____

9   When our bus passed Mary's house, we saw her father _____
    _____

10 The lifeguard ran down the beach when he heard somebody_____
    _____

Punctuating complex sentences

Put in the missing commas. *(10 marks)*

1   Yesterday in broad daylight the police caught two men trying to rob a bank.

2   The frightened rabbit stayed absolutely still hoping that the fox had not seen it.

3   My father the manager of the store starts work before 8 a.m.

4   Last night the temperature in most Welsh towns was above freezing-point. In Aberystwyth however it was minus four degrees.

5   Did you enjoy yourself at the party last Saturday Kate?

6   Although the concert lasted for over two hours the audience was captivated by the soloist who was only ten.

7   Not having seen her cousin for several years Sue was surprised to see how tall he was.

8   Birmingham is a very large city. In fact it is one of the largest in the United Kingdom.

9   When the phone rang Peter hurried to answer it hoping that it was his friend.

10 Leaping over the wall the frightened animal disappeared into the woods.

Unit 6 Punctuation

Key idea

Adding clauses increases the complexity of sentences, so more punctuation is required.

Using commas

Put in commas where necessary. The sentences show various different uses of commas. *(10 marks)*

1 The home of the Duke of Devonshire has 173 rooms and houses more than 60 types of clocks.

2 Paul go and find Mary please.

3 Worms are probably the most common bait for fish. If you expect to catch fish therefore you must be prepared to handle worms.

4 'Ugh! I'm not going to touch a worm' Katie said.

5 One of our neighbours Mrs Collins is a very experienced nurse.

6 Even if I were a billionaire I would not want to live alone in a huge isolated house.

7 Very few people read poetry books in their leisure time. Many modern pop songs however contain their own type of poetry and are very popular.

8 When tadpoles get older their tails get shorter their legs get longer and they gradually develop into very small frogs.

9 Pauline Taylor whose father is a maths teacher is always top of the class in maths not surprisingly.

10 If you're ready it's time for us to leave for the airport Grandad.

Using speech marks

Each of these unpunctuated sentences contains direct speech. Rewrite them, putting in the speech marks and other punctuation marks and capital letters that are necessary. *(10 marks)*

1 My friend said to me would you mind checking this letter for me please

2 I told her you've left an r out of preferred

3 Miss Lee told me you should have written chose and not choose

4 I heard Paul shout out wait for me Mike so we waited for him

5 If you've finished your homework my mother said you can watch the film on TV

6 when the performance ended the audience rose to their feet and shouted bravo

7 clamouring up the treacherous rocks the mountain rescuer cried hold on

8 can i follow you asked grace i dont know the way besides its dark

9 the wizard whose wand was misbehaving shook his finger and said abracadabra

10 louise rubbed her eyes yawned and mumbled whats the matter

More punctuation practice

Put in any necessary punctuation marks and capital letters. *(10 marks)*

1 its the end of march tomorrow remember to put your clocks on an hour

2 remember what people say in america spring forward fall back

3 in sentence 2 the word fall means autumn

4 there are 24 children in our class 14 boys and 10 girls

5 i think that jacket is a real bargain don't you mary

6 that was my first visit to a zoo I thought it was very interesting

7 come in sit down would you like a soft drink

8 some girls like to play netball or rounders others prefer hockey

9 the speaker promised the people many things more jobs higher pay longer holidays and lower taxes

10 don't forget the saying nothing ventured nothing gained

Unit 8 Active and passive verbs 2

Key idea

Verbs can be in the **active** or **passive** voice.

Look to the future

Read the two passages. Write in the *passive* future form of the verbs in brackets.
(10 marks)

A. Tomorrow part of the motorway (1)_____ (close) for urgent resurfacing. The work (2)_____ (complete) by 4 p.m., when the road (3)_____ (reopen) to traffic. While the road is closed, traffic (4)_____(divert). Notices (5)_____ (put) up to show motorists the route to follow.

B. Miss Harris told her class, "Our Sports Day will be on next Friday. It (6)_____ (hold) on the school field, starting at noon. All lessons will be (7)_____ (cancel) for the afternoon of that day. All parents (8)_____ (invite) to come. If bad weather is forecast, you (9)_____ (tell) and Sports Day (10)_____ (postpone) to the following week."

Will, may or must?

Read these sentences carefully. Then decide whether to put in *will*, *may* or *must*.
(10 marks)

1 This letter is urgent. It _____ be posted as soon as possible.

2 During a thunderstorm, don't shelter under a tree. It _____ be hit by lightning. If it is hit, you _____ be killed or seriously injured.

3 Be careful if you see an adder. It is a venomous snake with black zigzag marks on its top. Don't go near or touch an adder. If you do, you _____ be bitten. Then you _____ be taken to hospital. You _____ be given an antidote to fight the venom from the snake.

4 Check your bike before you go for a long ride. The brakes _____ be checked and the tyres _____ be pumped up if necessary.

5 When people return from a holiday overseas, their passports _____ be checked by an Immigration Officer. Then their luggage _____ be searched by a Customs Officer.

Active to passive

Change these sentences so that they contain *passive* verbs instead of active ones. Leave out the italic words. *(10 marks)*

1 *Somebody* stole Mr Jackson's car during the night.

2 Before the dentist drilled my tooth, *she* gave me an injection.

3 *Some workmen* pulled down that old factory last week.

4 *The strong wind* blew down two trees last night.

5 *Somebody* has just taken Mrs Sharpe to hospital.

6 *Two dustmen* collect our rubbish every Friday.

7 *People* grow a lot of apples in this part of the country.

8 *Sharks or other large fish* sometimes attack swimmers not far from the beach.

9 *The Mayor* will open the new school tomorrow.

10 *Several workmen* will redecorate our school during the holidays.

# Unit 9

Official language

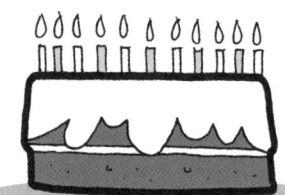

Key idea

Formal and official documents have certain language features that distinguish them from informal writing.

Informal: first person (personal); colloquial/slang vocabulary; use of contractions; short, simple sentences; exclamations, questions

Formal: third person (impersonal); technical, subject-specific vocabulary; no contractions; complex sentences; statements

Len Benton sent his friend, Mary Evans, a fake formal letter from a firm of solicitors when she wanted to borrow his bicycle. Mary decided to continue the game with Len. She sent him this invitation to her birthday party.

> On behalf of Miss Mary Evans, we have very considerable pleasure in requesting the pleasure of your company at a sumptuous festive social gathering of young attractive females and boisterous males to celebrate the eleventh anniversary of her blessed nativity.
>
> Please be informed accordingly that this joyful event will take place at Miss Evans' ancestral place of residence at 462 Rowan Road on Saturday 25 April, commencing punctually at 4 p.m. and drawing to a close by 8 p.m.
>
> To enable us to make adequate preparations, we would greatly appreciate it if you would kindly get in touch with us and indicate whether or not you will be able to join all concerned in this celebration. Kindly let us know what you decide before noon on 21 April so that our plans may be finalised well in advance. Alternatively, you may prefer to make your decision known directly to Mary (by phone, email, fax or in person).
>
> We are asked to pass on to all guests Mary's particular request that presents should not be brought or sent.

What do they mean?

Find and underline the expressions in Mary's invitation that have these meanings.
(10 marks)

1 are happy   3 party   5 birthday   7 home   9 would like
2 to invite   4 children   6 note (verb)   8 finishing   10 everybody

In translation

Len's brother asked him what was in the letter from Mary. Pretend you are Len. Tell your brother – in everyday English – what the main points of the invitation are. *(10 marks)*

_____
_____
_____
_____
_____
_____
_____

Keep it simple

Give the meaning of the expressions in italics. Use ordinary, everyday English that makes the meaning clear but uses fewer words. *(10 marks)*

1 Please *contact him in writing*. _____

2 Write your name here, *giving your surname and all given names*.
 _____

3 *In the event that* you are unable to come, bring a note when you recover.
 _____

4 Mike missed a lot of lessons at school *as a result* of illness.
 _____

5 Ask a parent or *the person who is legally responsible for looking after you* to write a note to your teacher, explaining why you were absent.
 _____

6 Peter cannot come today because he is *suffering from some illness*.
 _____

7 The *man who has been accused of robbery but has not yet been tried or convicted* will give evidence tomorrow.
 _____

8 Mr Macdonald is a farmer, so he would like to *wipe out and completely get rid of* all the rabbits on his farm.
 _____

9 Your claim for compensation will be *studied in detail to ascertain all aspects of the problem*.
 _____

10 You will be told *what is eventually decided by officials who look into your case*.
 _____

Unit 10 Forming complex sentences 2

Key idea

subordinate clause   main clause   subordinate clause

After the party, we all went straight home because it was late.

There are different types of subordinate clauses. They are linked to the main clause with connectives.

Adding connectives

Put one of the following connectives in each blank space below. *(10 marks)*

if	after	before	although	when	so
while	despite	provided	so	that	

1 I have a poster that reminds me to wash my hands _____ I have a meal, and to clean my teeth _____ I have eaten anything.

2 _____ Mum agrees, we're going to have a barbecue this evening _____ it doesn't rain.

3 The house in Elm Street was too expensive and _____ my parents decided not to buy it _____ we all liked it very much

4 You can borrow these videos but let me have them back _____ Mary can watch them _____ she returns from holiday.

5 The fire started _____ men were carrying out repairs. It destroyed the whole building _____ the efforts of the firemen.

Punctuating complex sentences

Punctuate these sentences correctly. Don't forget to put in capital letters where necessary. *(10 marks – 2 marks for each correct sentence)*

1 we expected toms friend to come at 5 pm however he didnt arrive until 530

2 in the middle of lunch a boy rushed into the canteen shouting fire fire

3 I put my books away and turned off the light then I went to bed

4 when the phone rang maya picked it up expecting to hear her friends voice

5 the answer peter gave although partially correct was not the right one

Joining sentences

Join each group of sentences to make one sentence. You can change, add or omit words. *(10 marks – 2.5 marks for each correct sentence)*

1 The rain stopped. We played in the garden. The grass was still wet. We were quite chilly.

2 The girl won lots of money. She gave half of it to charity. She is Janet's cousin.

3 This is the ring. My aunt gave it to me. I was ten then. It is beautiful.

4 Uncle George is over fifty. He completed the marathon. He raised lots of money for charity.

Making notes

🔑 Key idea

We make notes to extract the most important points from written words (such as information text) or spoken words (such as a telephone conversation or interview). We write them down in a shorter form.

Babysitting

You are babysitting for Mrs Done. You receive some phone calls and need to jot down notes so that you can write out messages for her. Make notes. *(10 marks)*

1. Is that Connie Jackson? Oh, well, maybe I could leave a message for her. My name is Peter Brown. I was going to call on her tomorrow at her office at about ten but something has come up, so I can't make it. Please ask her to phone my secretary at 099-438 tomorrow to fix another appointment. Thursday or Friday would be fine for me, ideally in the morning. Thanks. Goodbye.

2. Can I interest you in a good deal on double-glazing? This week we're offering … Oh, I see. Hmmm. Well, perhaps you'd tell her that Glunk Glass have this special offer next week, for seven days only. We're offering a discount of twenty-five per cent for two windows or more. If further details are needed, ask the lady to phone Andrew Brown at 047-738 any time. Thanks.

Customer services

You are learning the work in the Customer Services Department of a busy store. People phone, so you have to take notes and then tell the manager what the complaint is about. Read what these people said to you. Make notes. *(10 marks)*

1. My name's Ivy Trott. What's that? No, I'm not related to her. What I want to do is complain about the Milky Way Mousse. Don't get me wrong. I like them very much, but you never seem to have any in stock. What's happened? Are the staff eating them all? How come you've never got any on sale? Please ask somebody to order some more, pronto!

2 I want to complain about the tomatoes in your fruit and vegetable section. I usually buy a packet of six. Twice I've found that two of the tomatoes were bad underneath. They look all right on top but when you get them out – that's a different story. Maybe you could have a word with your order clerk or whoever does the ordering and change your supplier. I'll check up on them in the coming weeks and let you know if I see any improvement. I will be bringing back the two bad ones I bought this week and will expect a refund.

Local newspaper reporter

You are a reporter in the office of a local newspaper. You receive these phone calls. Make notes of the important points. *(10 marks)*

1 In the past week, six cars have been damaged by hooligans in Leo's car park. Each of them had a window broken. One had its tyres slashed. Three had the paintwork scratched badly. The damage occurs between about 10 p.m. and 6 a.m. I can tell you the names and addresses of a couple of louts who hang out there if you're interested.

2 You ought to investigate a house in Lufton Road. It's number 39 There's something fishy going on there. It's been empty for about six months, but recently the lights have been on and I've seen a lot of people coming and going with huge boxes at all hours of the day. There are often five or six lorries parked in the road at a time. There's a problem with burglary in our area at the moment. Perhaps the house is being used to store stolen goods.

unit 12 Writing a summary

Key idea

A summary is a re-telling in a shorter number of words of something you have read or heard.
- Summaries require writing in complete sentences.
- Summaries should include the main idea and important points only.

One-word summaries

In each case, give one word that summarises the group of words below. *(10 marks)*

1. a place where water is stored so that it can be sent to homes
   _____

2. walking along slowly and hardly lifting the feet off the ground
   _____

3. a long hole through a hill, often for a railway line
   _____

4. a place where people can keep their money and earn interest
   _____

5. a man or woman who looks after sick or injured people
   _____

6. wet stuff that comes trickling down from the clouds
   _____

7. biting and biting and biting (when the food is tough)
   _____

8. not liking to be delayed or kept waiting for anything
   _____

9. taken into custody (by a police officer)
   _____

10. in a way showing considerable skill
    _____

22

Headlines

Make up five newspaper headlines (of not more than six words each). *(10 marks – 2 marks for each one)*

1 A mineshaft has opened under a house in a village near Durham, causing half the house to disappear down the shaft. Luckily, the owners were in the other half of the house and were not hurt – but they were shocked.

    _____

2 A large black animal, similar to a panther, has been seen by a farmer in a field near Taunton. Several sheep have been killed in the vicinity recently.

    _____

3 Cricketer Jason Foley has just scored 500 not out in a test match against Australia. He has earned a five-figure bonus for his achievement.

    _____

4 A girl, aged 12, fell at home, hit her head on a stone floor and became unconscious. Her mother dialled 999 but the ambulance did not arrive until an hour later. By that time, the girl was gravely ill. She died shortly after she was taken to hospital. Her parents were outraged and very angry at the delay.

    _____

5 A venomous spider was found in a bunch of grapes imported from South Africa. The purchaser spotted the spider and took it to a laboratory where it was examined and then killed. It was found to be extremely harmful. The store which sold the grapes has apologised and promised to inspect imports more thoroughly.

    _____

What can you remember?

Write a summary of each of the things below. Use a single sentence each time. Do not use more than twenty words in each sentence. *(10 marks – 2.5 marks for each sentence)*

1 A recent lesson which you enjoyed at school _____
   _____

2 What you did yesterday from 5 p.m. until the time you went to bed _____
   _____

3 The last television programme you watched _____
   _____

4 Your favourite book _____
   _____

Editing

Key idea

Editing involves reviewing and improving our own (or someone else's) writing to make it more effective.

Using more effective words

You are editing a composition written by a friend. Suggest two more effective words that could be used instead of the words in italics. Your words do not have to be synonyms of the italic words, but they should be suitable for the situation.

(10 marks – 0.5 mark for each suitable answer)

1   A group of children ran away in front of us. When we were nearly at the corner, a woman *came* out of her house. She was upset and waved her arms angrily at us.

    _____   _____

2   'Go away! Get out of here!' she *said to* us *loudly*.

    _____   _____
    _____   _____

3   The policeman *looked* at us. His face *indicated* that trouble was coming.

    _____   _____
    _____   _____

4   The old man *moved* painfully towards the receptionist.

    _____   _____

5   Mary wore a *nice* outfit to her friend's party.

    _____   _____

6   The tornado *pulled apart* the town, leaving a trail of destruction behind it.

    _____   _____

7   The poor animal *moved* towards us on its three good legs as if *asking* us to help.

    _____   _____
    _____   _____

Correcting errors

The following sentences are taken from a report by a pupil about the school canteen. Edit the sentences by correcting any mistakes in them. Write out the sentences correctly. *(10 marks – 0.5 mark for each correction)*

1 In the coarse of our investigations, we watched pupils had lunch on sevral days.

2 We noticed that some pupil had to queue a long time before they could obtained there food.

3 We therefore suggest that there should be two seperate sessions for lunch, the younger children can eat 20 minutes earlier then the oldest pupils.

4 This will also prevent the food to becoming cold and will enable the servers to work more careful, they are all in favour of this change.

5 We asked each pupil to complete a questionaire about the food, we used the information from them to produce the lists in Apendix 3

6 The tables what the pupils sit at are to crowded, so we recommend that only six pupils sit at each table, this will be possible if we have two sessions instead of one.

Using headings

(10 marks)

A classmate prepared to write a report on her school canteen. She jotted down these points:

amount of food	crowding	behaviour of pupils	servers
tables	pupil satisfaction	quality of food	cooks
cost of food	seating	cleanliness/hygiene	taste
(un)healthy food	hours/time	queues	waste

She showed you her notes and asked you for your opinion on arranging the points.

1 Suggest **five** main headings under which most or all of the points can be put.

_____
_____
_____
_____
_____

The pupils in Miss Wilson's class asked her if they could have a class picnic, so she asked them to plan the arrangements for a picnic. One pupil wrote about the following points but did not put them under any headings or in any clear order.

date	bus/car/train/coach	music/songs	weather – alternative indoors
times	food	drinks	parents – inform, come?
place	games	cost	activities

2 Suggest **five** main headings for a plan for the picnic.

_____
_____
_____
_____
_____

Unit 14 Conditional sentences

Key idea

A conditional sentence says that one thing depends on another. Conditional sentences usually contain the words **if** or **unless**. The "if" or "unless" part of the sentence is a special type of subordinate clause called a **conditional clause**.

      conditional clause   main clause

<u>*If you tickle me*</u>, <u>*I will laugh.*</u>

What happens?

Complete these sentences in any sensible way. They are about habitual (usual) actions. *(10 marks – 2 marks for each correct sentence)*

1. If you leave ice out of a fridge, _____
2. If a player hits another player during a game of football, _____ _____
3. If people find that they have mice in their home, _____ _____
4. If it rains while the sun is shining, _____
5. If I'm very thirsty during the night, _____

What will probably happen?

Put in the right form of the verbs in brackets. The sentences are about things that may, can or probably will happen in future. *(5 marks – 0.5 mark for each correct answer)*

1. If a young child _____ (play) with matches at home, he or she _____ (start) a fire.
2. If it rains on Saturday, our Sports Day _____ (postpone). Then it _____ (hold) on 23 June.
3. If you _____ (eat) too much food, you _____ (put) on weight.
4. If you both stand on that table at the same time, it _____ (probably collapse) and you _____ (break) something.
5. If the rain doesn't stop soon, all this area _____ (flood) and we _____ (force) to leave our home.

Giving advice

We can use **If I were you ...** to give advice:

If I were you,	I wouldn't eat so much.
	I wouldn't bother to answer that email.
	I would be honest about it.

What advice can you give these friends or relatives? *(10 marks – 2 marks for each suitable answer)*

1 Dave says he always feels tired in the morning. He admits that he rarely goes to bed before 11 p.m. because his parents let him stay up to watch films.

   _____
   _____

2 You are visiting an aunt with your brother or sister. You have both been offered a cup of coffee, but you have declined the coffee politely. Your brother or sister is not sure whether or not to try drinking it and asks your advice.

   _____
   _____

3 A friend says she has several unwanted jigsaw puzzles at home. She is not sure whether to take them to a charity shop or just to throw them away. What do you advise?

   _____
   _____
   _____

4 A friend's family are going to spend a few days in Paris during the holidays. They can't decide whether to go by rail, ferry or air. Your friend mentioned this to you and said, "What would you do?"

   _____
   _____

5 A friend goes to a different school from yours. He tells you that he has noticed that two older boys are bullying younger pupils and making them pay money nearly every day. He is not sure what, if anything, he should do. He has asked for your advice. What do you suggest?

   _____
   _____

Other ways of showing a condition

We can also show a condition by making sentences like these:

You can go	provided that	you return before dark.
You can play with them	as long as	you're back by 700 p.m.
It's all right for you to go	on condition that	you are not late home again.

Use the information in each pair of sentences to make one sentence using one of the connectives in the second column above. You can change, omit or add words.
(5 marks)

1. You can go to Tom's house. You must be back here by 800 p.m.
   _____

2. You can borrow my bike. You must return it on Saturday.
   _____

3. Tom can stay with us for the weekend. His parents must agree.
   _____

4. I'll help you. Don't argue all the time.
   _____

5. We can have a picnic on Saturday. The weather must be fine then.
   _____

Narrative writing

 **Key idea** •

The purpose of a narrative text is to tell a story. Although individual stories can be very different, they all have some common structural and language features.

Zangram by C. J. Salter: extract 1

Read this extract from *Zangram*. Then answer the questions below. *(10 marks)*

1   The Logan family pulled wearily into a deserted car park not far from Stonehenge. Jack Logan, exhausted after driving for nine hours, said to his wife, "I need a rest."
    "Good idea," his wife replied. "I told Sylvia we wouldn't be down 'til
5 noon."
    Jack Logan glanced in the rear-view mirror. His children, Daniel and Claire, were sleeping soundly. So he settled down and was soon asleep himself.
    Some time later, Claire stirred. The car seemed to be moving, but then
10 the movement stopped. She heard her dad snoring contentedly, and drifted back to sleep.
    On board Spacecraft 462, the doors closed and a message flashed back to Zangram, far beyond Earth's solar system: "Mission completed. 20 specimens including four bipeds in a metal shell." The spaceship rose silently
15 from a field near Stonehenge and hurtled off into space. It carried with it the Logan family, their car, two inquisitive dogs, a deeply resentful cat and other specimens destined for examination and display in the Zangram national zoo.

1   In paragraph one, which word repeats the idea expressed by "wearily"? *(1 mark)*

_____

2   What were Mrs Logan's exact words when she spoke to Sylvia? *(1 mark)*

_____

3   What is missing before "Good idea" (line 4)? Why has it been left out? *(2 marks)*

_____

4   What adverb could we use instead of each of the following? (The adverb need not have the same meaning as the given word, but it must fit the situation.) *(4 marks)*

   a) soundly (line 7) _____   c) silently (line 14) _____

   b) contentedly (line 10) _____   d) deeply (line 16) _____

5   a) What does "inquisitive" tell us about the dogs? b) Why was the cat "resentful"? *(2 marks)*

   _____

Zangram: extract 2

Read this continuation of *Zangram*. Then answer the questions about it.
(10 marks)

> 1   When the Logan family woke up, they discovered they were in a huge glass dome. They were unaware, however, of the battery of tests and examinations that the Zangrams had carried out on them over a period of several days.
>
> 5   Outside the dome, a crowd of Zangrams watched the family through one-way glass. A notice outside the dome said, when translated into English, "On loan from Planet 264S/36 for 30 days". Of course, the Logans knew nothing of this. They believed that somehow they had been kidnapped.
>
>   "Well, at least we're alive," said Mrs Logan, trying to console her
> 10 children. "Sooner or later, we'll find out where we are and why we're here."
>
>   She was right. They found out the next day when the Zangrams had finally solved the riddle of Earth language and began to communicate with them.

1   What happened to the Logan family before they were put on display? *(2 marks)*

   _____

2   Why does the writer start a new paragraph in three places after the first paragraph? Give a reason why each of the three paragraphs has been started. *(3 marks)*

   _____

   _____

   _____

3   How does the phrase that begins the second paragraph link it to the first paragraph? *(2 marks)*

   _____

4 What does the pronoun "this" in line 8 refer to? *(1 mark)*

_____

5 How does the writer create a dramatic effect at the beginning of the last paragraph? *(2 marks)*

_____

Zangram: extract 3

Now read extract 3 and answer the questions about it. *(10 marks)*

> 1   When the Logans woke up in the car park at Stonehenge, they were puzzled to find their car turned round. They knew something odd had happened, but what? They drove on to Cornwall in some confusion. Their bewilderment deepened when they finally reached the home of Jack's brother and rang the
> 5   doorbell. Tony Logan opened the door and stared at them in a mixture of astonishment and horror.
>   "Where have you been?" he said at last. "We were expecting you a month ago! We checked with your neighbours. We even informed the police because …"
> 10   "A month ago!" echoed Jack Logan. "We agreed July 10th and here we are."
>   Tony stared at his brother, trying to decide whether he was joking or not. "But today is August 10th," he pointed out. "Anyway, come in. You're welcome at any time – even when you're officially 'missing, presumed dead'."
>   Mrs Logan and the children went in. Jack went back to the car to unpack
> 15   the luggage. What he saw in the boot proved that something very strange had occurred.

1 What is similar about the ways in which extracts 1, 2 and 3 end? *(2 marks)*

_____

2 "We even informed the police because …" Why does the author insert …? *(1 mark)*

_____

3 Find five *different* uses of capital letters in the extract. *(5 marks)*

_____

_____

4 Write a sentence saying what Mr Logan found in the boot. *(2 marks)*

_____

Unit 17 Describing past events

🔑 Key idea

The purpose of writing a recount is to tell about a past event. Recount texts have some common structural and language features that help to identify them.

Time connectives

Read the account of a football match below. Put in ten different linking words or expressions. Choose from those below. *(10 marks)*

right up to the final whistle	shortly afterwards	at the start of the game
within the first ten minutes	ten minutes later	for the rest of the first half
during the half-time break	at half-time	ten minutes from the end
	immediately	

(1)_____ yesterday, Newtown were confidently expected to beat Oldtown by at least two goals. Newtown forced two corners (2)_____, but failed to score. Oldtown struck back but Jordan's shot was wide. (3)_____, Ken Teale put Newtown one up when he headed home a cross from Ojuro. Play was restricted to the centre of the field (4)_____ with Newtown slightly superior. (5)_____ the score remained Newtown 1 – Oldtown 0

Newtown manager, Joe Kellick, gave his men a pep-talk (6)_____. The players responded with raids on the Oldtown goal, during which Ken Teale scored his second goal. (7)_____ Oldtown veteran, Paul Cranston, scored for Oldtown. Stung by this unexpected goal, Newtown launched another series of attacks (8)_____ and were rewarded when Ojuro scored Newtown's third goal.

(9)_____ Tom Baxter shot wide for Oldtown. Defences dominated the game (10)_____.

Final score: Newtown 3 – Oldtown 1

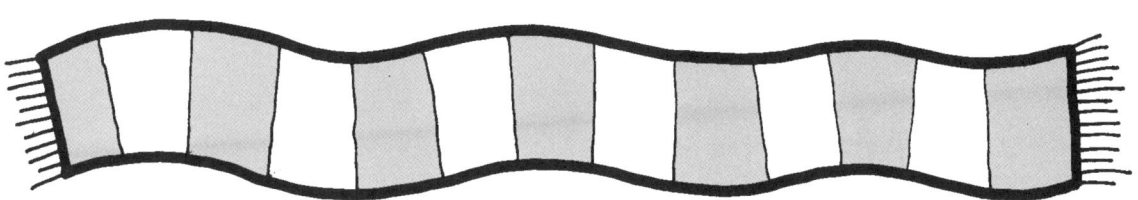

Exploring language

Read 'Hot water' and then answer the questions about it. *(20 marks)*

Hot water

Sue went to visit her grandfather, aged 90, in a remote rural district. Grandad cooked a very tasty lunch. However, when Sue put the plates and cutlery on the table, she noticed some tiny brown specks on her plate. She studied the plate thoughtfully for a few moments.

"Grandad," she asked hesitantly. "Are you … Are these plates clean?"

"Of course they are," Grandad replied quickly. "They're as clean as hot water can get them. That's for sure. Enjoy your meal and don't worry about the plates."

In the evening, Sue helped Grandad to prepare supper. She was hungry and was just about to put the food on the plates when she saw a thin piece of something on one of the plates. It looked like scrambled egg.

"Grandad," she said firmly. "Are you absolutely sure these plates are clean?"

"No doubt about it," Grandad said with a smile. "They're as clean as hot water can make them. I can guarantee that."

A few minutes later, a neighbour approached Grandad's house. Immediately his dog started to bark furiously. Grandad shouted angrily at the dog, "Cut that out, Hotwater! No more barking! Go and lay down! It's only Jim. You know him."

"I call her 'Hotwater'," Grandad explained to Sue, "because she always gets me into trouble."

"Ugh!" Sue thought. "I wonder if … I think I've been had."

"Grandad," she said quietly, "I'll wash the dishes tonight."

1   a) Underline any ten adjectives in the passage. *(5 marks)*

    b) Choose six of the adjectives and give words opposite in meaning to them. *(3 marks)*

    _____   _____

    _____   _____

    _____   _____

2   Choose three verbs used in the past tense in the passage. Write them down and then write the present and future tenses of each. *(3 marks)*

    _____

    _____

    _____

3   At the end of the third sentence, what one word can we insert after "plate" to turn the following sentence into a subordinate clause?_____ *(1 mark)*

4   Suggest a reason why Sue was hesitant when she first asked Grandad if the plates were clean? *(1 mark)*

    _____

5   Complete the sentence. *(1 mark)*

    "In line 6, the writer uses 'as … as' to_____

6   a) Write down any six adverbs in the passage. *(3 marks)*

    _____   _____

    _____   _____

    _____   _____

    b) Choose any four of the adverbs and write down words opposite in meaning to them. *(2 marks)*

7   What did Sue mean when she said, "I think I've been had"? *(1 mark)*

    _____

35

unit 18 Giving instructions

Key idea

Instructions, directions and descriptions of procedures all have to be written clearly and concisely so they are easy to follow. Features such as sequenced and numbered steps, imperative verbs and sequencing connectives are common to this type of writing.

Checklist

Paul wrote the following checklist for maintaining his bike. Read it and then answer the questions about it. *(15 marks)*

> Checklist for maintaining bicycles
> 1 Check <u>brake</u> cables. Do brake blocks make good contact with rims of wheels?
> 2 Is <u>bell</u> fastened firmly? Does it work properly?
> 3 Check if front and rear <u>lights</u>. Replace battry or check dynamo if necessary.
> 4 <u>Chain</u> - tighten and see if any oil is needed.
> 5 <u>Saddle</u> - make sure it is at the right height and comfortable.
> 6 <u>Carrier</u> - check that nuts holding carrier are not lose. Tighten?
> 7 Check nuts holding <u>wheels</u> in place. Tighten or replace if necessary.
> 8 Check air in <u>tyres</u>; check for slow punctures.
> 9 Grease or oil any points that need lubricating, e.g. wheel <u>axils</u>.
> 10 Check that <u>tyre valves</u> are working properly.
> 11 Buy <u>padlock</u> with at least two keys. Get extra keys cut?

1 In step 2, are "firmly" and "properly" adjectives or adverbs?
   _____ *(2 marks)*

2 In step 3, what words are missing from the first sentence?
   _____ *(2 marks)*

3 How could Paul do step 5? _____ *(2 marks)*

4 Find four misspelt words and correct them. *(4 marks)*
   _____ _____
   _____ _____

5 Rewrite step 2 as a single statement with an imperative verb. *(2 marks)*
   _____

6   Which two steps could you combine so that there are only ten steps? *(2 marks)*

7   What is the purpose of step 11? *(1 mark)*

Defrosting a freezer

Rewrite Gran's instructions for how to defrost a freezer. Set them out in the right order using no more than ten steps. Leave out points that are not necessary.
(15 marks)

> Well, of course, you have to make sure that you don't make a mess in the kitchen. We don't want any water left on the floor to make the place slippery. That's how Grandad broke a leg a few years ago. Get a few old towels (there are plenty at the bottom of the airing-cupboard) and take them to the freezer. Oh, yes, you'll need a pail or a saucepan to put the water in. Put one of the towels on the floor in front of the freezer to catch the drips. Now, where was I? Ah, yes, empty the freezer. There are only a couple of packets in it now. Stick them in the fridge. Turn off the electricity. Open the freezer wide. Put a couple of towels inside to soak up the water. If you're in a hurry, put a bowl of hot water on a shelf in the freezer. It will help to thaw out the ice. You can poke any pieces of ice free if you like but it's not necessary.
>
> Leave the freezer door open and just be patient. When the ice has all gone, wring out the towels. Clean and dry the freezer. Get rid of any water. Then put the packets back in the freezer and turn it on. Easy!

Writing reports

Key idea

Report texts present information on a subject. They describe things as they are. They often feature present-tense verbs, descriptive adjectives and adverbs, and headings and subheadings.

The breakfast report

(10 marks)

1   "Write a report about breakfast in your family," said the teacher to Paul's class. If you were in the class, how would you arrange your ideas? Think of headings for three paragraphs. *(3 marks)*

    _____

    _____

    _____

> Breakfast by Paul
> We have three different kinds of breakfast, classified according to how it is eaten.
> My favourite is a "sitting-down" breakfast. It is a leisurely event on Saturday and Sunday because I do not have to get up early. It includes cereal, fried eggs, beans, mushrooms, toast and jam and a big glass of orange juice.
> A "standing-up" breakfast involves a drink, toast and a piece of fruit. I usually have this on school days because I have less time.
> When I forget to set the alarm and am late for school, I have to have an "on-the-move" breakfast. I shoot out of the house, buy a chocolate bar and eat it before the bell rings.

2   Write paragraph headings for Paul's report above. *(3 marks)*

    _____

    _____

    _____

3   What part of speech is each of these words as it is used in Paul's report? *(4 marks)*
    a) classified _____   b) leisurely _____
    c) usually _____   d) shoot _____

The rodent report

This is part of a report on squirrels, written by Sally, age 11 Read it and then answer the questions about it. *(10 marks)*

> ## Grey squirrels
> **Where they came from**
>
> Grey squirrels were brought to Britain from America many years ago and kept in zoos. Some excaped and spread to both rural and urban areas. They have now driven red squirrels away.
>
> _____
>
> They prefer to eat seeds, berries and especially nuts, so they can often be found near oak, beech and other nut trees. However, they also eat birds' eggs and baby birds. Therefore, the presents of squirrels often leads to the absence of birds since they cannot nest safely.
>
> **How they behave**
>
> Grey squirrels are active during the day and do not hibernate in winter. They are naturaly shy, but not when it comes to food. In some towns, squirrels in parks are so tame that they will take peanuts, if offered, from people's hands.
>
> **The problems they cause**
>
> Grey squirrels (in fact, all kinds of squirrels) can be pests. They raid berries and other fruit from bushes and trees in poeple's gardens. They also gnaw and eat bark, which leads to the death of trees.

1. a) Circle the passive verb in the first paragraph. *(1 mark)*
   b) Why is the verb not active? *(1 mark)* _____

2. Fill in the missing subheading for the second paragraph. *(2 marks)*

3. Draw a box around each of the connectives in the second paragraph. (Do not include "and".) *(2 marks)*

4. Find the four misspelled words in the report. Draw a line through each one and write the correctly spelled word above. *(2 marks)*

5. In the last sentence of the third paragraph, underline the main clause once and the subordinate clause twice. *(2 marks)*

Write a worm report

(10 marks)

Here are some notes about worms.
1 Think of four different headings under which you could group the notes.
2 Then write a four-paragraph report using the notes.

- Do not like light
- Eat dead leaves and soil
- Has complete digestive system
- Help plants to grow
- Live underground
- Long, soft bodies with head and tail end
- Make tunnels to move about
- No bones, eyes, legs
- Soil leaves body making worm "casts"
- Useful creatures – tunnels bring air to soil
- Use muscles and hairs on skin to move
- Take nutrients from soil as it passes through body

WORMS

Paragraph 1 heading:_____

Paragraph 2 heading:_____

Paragraph 3 heading:_____

Paragraph 4 heading:_____

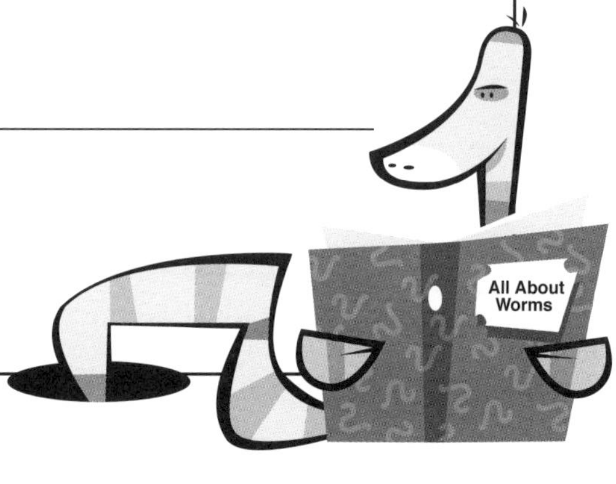

Unit 20: Persuasive writing

 **Key idea**

Persuasive writing aims to influence the reader towards a particular opinion. It often uses emotional words, figurative devices and imperative verbs.

Email scam

Mrs Stone received this email, which is full of mistakes. Fortunately, she knew it was not from her bank at all, but an attempt by someone to find out her details illegally. Read it and answer the questions. *(10 marks)*

```
Subject: Confirm your details to avoid immediate cancellation to your
account.

Yesterday the bank have a failure of its software this resulted in a
lost of customer data. To help you to avoid from fraud, kindly connect
with the link below to confirm your account registration data, this is
obligatory to protect your account.

Please do not answer to this message. Fill in the form "Confirmation
of Acount Details".
```

1 Which words in the "subject" are meant to frighten the receiver? *(1 mark)*

2 Find an incorrect verb tense. Explain why it is wrong and correct it. *(2 marks)*

3 Find two places where punctuation is wrong or missing. Correct them. *(2 marks)*

4 Find and correct four expressions in which prepositions are used wrongly. *(2 marks)*

5 Find and correct two spelling mistakes. *(2 marks)*

6 Why does the sender of the email put in the sentence, "This is obligatory to protect your account"? *(1 mark)*

**The mighty T-watch is here:
hep, handy, helpful!**

It's COOL and it could be yours!

On one side, it's a watch.
No need to look at it.

Press the button and it tells you the time. Now that's really something – but there's more!

On the other side? A nifty recorder. Up to 10 minutes talktime. No need to take notes.

**Move up to the in-crowd!
ORDER NOW
before they're all snapped up.**

"I love it!" says pop star Kati Lane.

Football legend, Mike O'Shea:
"I wouldn't be without mine!"

An advertisement

Read the advertisement above and then answer these questions. *(10 marks)*

1 Which slang words in the advertisment mean "up-to-date, fashionable"? *(1 mark)*

2 What figurative device is used in the second line? *(1 mark)*

3 Why is "COOL" put in capital letters? *(1 mark)*

4 "On the other side? A nifty recorder." Explain why the writer doesn't use complete sentences. *(2 marks)*

5 Why does the advertiser use the word "nifty" instead of "clever"? *(1 mark)*

6 Explain the purpose of the pictures. *(2 marks)*

7 Give one example each of two different verb forms used in the advertisement. *(1 mark)*

8 In the first draft of this advertisement, the advertiser wrote : "Keep up with the in-crowd". Why did she change this to "Move up to the in-crowd"? *(1 mark)*

Getting involved

Miss Benson's class wrote to their local council following three traffic accidents near their school. Read their first draft below and then answer the questions.
(10 marks)

> In the passed six months, there have been three horrific traffic acidents near our school, each time somebody was knocked down by a speeding motorist. We beg the Council to do something to make Bridge Street safer.
>
> We would like to recommend four crucial measures. First of all, we hope the Council can put some speed bumps in the road to slow down traffic. Secondly, we need a pedestran crossing outside our school. Thirdly, it would be a good idea to errect warning sines at each end of Bridge Street, finally, we think that cars should not be aloud to park outside our school for longer than 15 minutes during 8–9 a.m. and 3–4 p.m. on school days.

1. Why do the children mention accidents in their letter? *(1 mark)*

2. Give two examples of powerful, emotive words in the letter. Why do the children use them? *(2 marks)*

3. Find and correct six spelling mistakes in the draft letter. *(3 marks)*

4. Find two places where a comma should be replaced by a full stop. *(1 mark)*

5. Find a passive verb in the first paragraph. *(1 mark)*

6. List the sequencing connectives used in the second paragraph. *(1 mark)*

7. How might the children revise the layout of the second paragraph so that their suggestions are clearer? *(1 mark)*

Writing discussion texts

🔑 Key idea

Discussion texts give a balanced presentation of all the various positions that are held about an issue or topic – for example, both sides of an argument.

Television: points of view

"Does television do more harm than good?" Read the first draft of what one pupil wrote and then answer the questions about it. *(10 marks)*

1 Most television shows have a bad influence to viewers, especially young ones. They use swear words and bad language most of the time. Violence is common in "soaps" and are regarded as a model or example to teenagers.
   On the other hand, documentries are both educational and intresting. There is always
5 something new for viewers to learn as long as they can stay awake. Oddly enough, the cartoons are usually OK. They are always amusing without setting a bad example. Sports programmes are also worth watching and do not cause no harm or offence.
   Maybe the only fair answer to the question is that the affect of TV depends upon the individual. If you have firm principals, you can always chose wisely. I hope that television
10 channels will clean up their act, but I won't hold my breathe waiting for that to happen.

1 What more accurate word should the writer use instead of "most" in lines 1 and 2? *(1 mark)*
   _____

2 In lines 1 and 3, replace "to" with correct prepositions. *(2 marks)*
   _____   _____

3 Explain and correct the error of agreement in the third sentence. *(1 mark)*
   _____

4 Explain and correct the error in the last sentence of the second paragraph.
   (1 mark)
   _____

5 Correct six spelling mistakes in the last two paragraphs. *(3 marks)*
   _____

6 Is the writer's discussion well-balanced? Explain your answer. *(2 marks)*
   _____

Maths – or no maths?

"Should children be allowed to decide whether they want to study maths or not?" Read the first draft of what one pupil wrote and then answer the questions about it. *(10 marks)*

1   Some people say that we do not need maths in our daily lifes because calculaters and computers can give us all the answers. I don't agree to that because sometimes if we don't know any maths it is easy for crooks to cheat us. Also we need maths whenever we buy or sell anything and maybe we have no calculator available.

5   On the other hand, it is true that algebra and geometry can be too difficult to some children and they become confused and fed up. Then they may even hate the subject and start to behave badly at school. Perhaps the right thing to do is to make basic maths compulsery up to, say, the age of 14 and to make it optional after that. If somebody is no good at maths (even when he or she tries very hard), it is a waist of time to force the

10 person to continue to study the subject.

1 Find and correct four spelling errors: two in each paragraph *(2 marks)*

2 Correct the mistakes in the use of prepositions in lines 2 and 5 *(1 mark)*

3 What more formal words could the writer use instead of "crooks" (line 3) and "fed up" (line 6)? *(1 mark)*

4 How many points for each side of the argument does the writer give? What are they? *(4 marks)*

5 Do you agree with the writer's conclusion? Give reasons for your answer. *(2 marks)*

Should it be a crime to kill any wild animal?

(10 marks)

Put a suitable word in each blank space. *(7 marks – 0.5 mark for each correct answer)*

I am in favour of protecting wild animals, but there (1)_____ two main reasons (2)_____ I do not think it (3)_____ be a crime to kill any wild animal. Firstly, sometimes it is (4)_____ to kill wild animals such as mice, rats and rabbits. (5)_____ we do not kill some of them, they will increase (6)_____ cause serious problems. A (7)_____ reason is that sometimes wild animals, such (8)_____ boars, foxes, badgers and deer, increase and (9)_____ a threat to farmers. Then it is necessary to kill some of (10)_____.

We must also remember (11)_____ some farmers keep cattle, sheep, deer, goats and (12)_____ animals for their milk or meat. Are these wild animals? If somebody kills a wild pony on Dartmoor (13)_____ that a crime? As I said earlier, I think some wild animals should be protected, but making it a crime to kill one is not the (14)_____ way of doing it.

- **Do you think it should be a crime to kill wild animals? Give two reasons for your answer.** *(3 marks)*

_____
_____
_____
_____
_____

Investigating English expressions

 **Key idea** ....

Investigating language is the best way to find out how it works.

American English ....

(16 marks)

Americans speak English, but many of their words differ from British English. Do you know what they're talking about? Put the right British word by each American word below. *(8 marks – 0.5 mark for each correct answer)*

| taxi   pavement   sweets   dummy (for a baby)   nappy   trousers |
| autumn   boot (of a car)   lorry   curtains   petrol   sweet biscuits |
| lift   handbag   queue   tap (for water) |

1 cab _____

2 line _____

3 fall _____

4 truck _____

5 diaper _____

6 purse _____

7 candy _____

8 pants _____

9 trunk (of a car) _____

10 gas(oline) _____

11 pacifier _____

12 cookies _____

13 faucet _____

14 sidewalk _____

15 drapes _____

16 elevator _____

Now find out for yourself the British words for these American words. *(8 marks)*

17 drugstore _____

18 closet _____

19 stove _____

20 hood (of a car) _____

21 vacation _____

22 garbage _____

23 movies _____

24 buck (money) _____

Investigating idioms

Put the right idiom on each line below. *(14 marks)*

- a Tartar
- eyewash
- a close shave
- a mouthpiece
- a square peg in a round hole
- a rough diamond
- a pig in a poke
- a fool's paradise
- a blank cheque
- a fly in the ointment
- a red herring
- a hornets' nest
- soft soap
- a white lie

1 A _____ is an untrue statement which is made for good reasons, for example to protect an innocent person.

2 _____ is something (usually a statement) meant to deceive people or hide something wrong.

3 _____ is a person who is very difficult to deal with even if you have some advantage over them. Many years ago, if you captured this person in a battle, he would prove a troublesome prisoner.

4 _____ is something which is meant to deceive you, perhaps by making you look in the wrong direction when trying to solve a problem.

5 _____ is permission to do as you like, for example to spend as much money as you like because the cheque has been signed but no amount has been put in.

6 If you spend a lot of time dreaming about winning a lottery, you may live in _____, thinking about something nice which will never happen.

7 If you buy _____, you buy something (such as a pig tied up in a sack) before you have had a chance to inspect it.

8 _____ is flattery.

9 _____ is somebody who appears tough or lacking in manners, but is really very kind and generous.

10 If a person is in a job that does not suit him or her, we may say that the person is _____.

11 _____ is an obstacle to a plan.

12 Sometimes we call a narrow escape _____.

13 _____ is somebody who speaks on behalf of another person or organisation, often to give excuses or reasons for an action.

14 _____ is a source of possible trouble because if you interfere you may create a worse situation.

Key Grammar is a brand new resource, specifically planned to cover all the key grammar objectives in self-contained units of work. The pupil books feature:

- clear, progressive units covering all key learning objectives
- plenty of practice and consolidation work
- opportunities to challenge and extend children's learning
- a clear mark scheme
- exercises in an appropriate context, with engaging illustrations

The workbooks provide activities for additional practice, differentiation, and homework. The important language skills coverage in **Key Grammar** is complemented by two associated series: **Key Comprehension** and **Key Spelling** – up-to-date and engaging resources which reinforce key teaching points and enable children to practise, consolidate and extend their learning. For further information about **Key Comprehension** and **Key Spelling** call our Customer Services Department on **(+44) (0)1865 888000**.